C000116541

Upper
Intermediate
Matters

JAN BELL
ROGER GOWER

Longman

Contents chart

Grammar	Vocabulary	Pronunciation
Form and function; functional English; verb forms and time; revision	Plurals; describing people	Words from the text: phonemic transcription; word stress
Review of the present; habit in the past; *used to (do)* or *be used to (doing)?*; the definite article	Prefixes; word building; compound nouns	
Present, Present Perfect or Past?; duration; Present Perfect Simple or Continuous?	Entertainment; intensifying adjectives; adjectives and prepositions	Silent letters
Sequence of tenses; Past Perfect Simple or Continuous?; narrative forms	Phrasal verbs; common errors; verbs and prepositions; places	
Mixed question forms; less direct and reported questions; question tags; word order	Men and women; synonyms and antonyms	Question tags
Obligation; advice	Collocation; medical terms	Connected speech
Talking about the future; future time expressions	American English; prepositional phrases; collocation; forming adjectives and adverbs	
Future Continuous or Perfect?; future review; complex sentences	Words often confused; prepositions of time; idiomatic expressions; compound adjectives	
Review of the article; *could / (was/were) able to / managed to; used for; as/like*	Phrasal verbs; animals	
Present, Present Perfect or Past?; question forms; modals of obligation; future forms	Word building; prepositions; phrasal verbs; definitions	Dictation
Mixed conditional forms; *wish* and *if only*	Collocation; phrasal verbs; word association	Dictation
Past conditional and *wish; wish* and *if only*; criticisms (*should (not) have*)	Crime and punishment; nouns and prepositions	
The passive; pronouns; *have (get)* something done	Idiomatic expressions; newspaper headlines	
Verb + object + *to* + base form; *-ing* or *to?*; expressing preferences	Connotation; ambiguity; proverbs	
Quantity; compounds of *some, any, no, every; each, another, both, either,* etc.	Numbers; idioms	Words with the same spelling
Modals; reference words	Word building; similes; foreign words and phrases	
Reported speech; direct speech; reporting verbs	Adjectives and nouns; synonyms and antonyms; phrasal verbs	
Defining relative clauses; defining and non-defining relative clauses; participle clauses; adjectives ending in *-ing* and *-ed*	Word building; prepositional phrases; confusing words	Vowel sounds
Review of verb forms; conditionals; *wish*; modals; spot the errors; which is correct?	Colloquial language; test your vocabulary	

• Memories •

READING

1 Read the text below. Then look at the pictures and tick the one which best matches the description of the teacher. Use a dictionary where necessary.

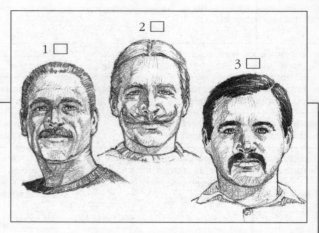

We called them masters in those days, not teachers, and at St Peter's the one I feared most of all, apart from the Headmaster, was Captain Hardcastle.

5 This man was slim and wiry and he played football. On the football field he wore white running shorts and white gymshoes and short white socks. His legs were as hard and thin as ram's legs and the skin around his calves was
10 almost exactly the colour of mutton fat. The hair on his head was not ginger. It was brilliant dark vermilion, like a ripe orange, and it was plastered back with immense quantities of brilliantine in the same fashion
15 as the Headmaster's. The parting in his hair was a white line straight down the middle of the scalp, so straight it could only have been made with a ruler. On either side of the parting you could see the comb tracks
20 running back through the greasy orange hair like little tramlines.

Captain Hardcastle sported a moustache that was the same colour as his hair, and oh what a moustache it was! A truly terrifying sight, a
25 thick orange hedge that sprouted and flourished between his nose and upper lip and ran clear across his face from the middle of one cheek to the middle of the other. But this was not one of those nailbrush moustaches, all
30 short and clipped and bristly. Nor was it long and droopy in the walrus style. Instead it was curled most splendidly upwards all the way along as though it had had a permanent wave put into it. Behind the moustache there lived
35 an inflamed and savage face with a deeply corrugated brow that indicated a very limited intelligence. 'Life is a puzzlement,' the corrugated brow seemed to be saying, 'and the world is a dangerous place. All men are
40 enemies and small boys are insects that will turn and bite you if you don't get them first and squash them hard.'

Captain Hardcastle was never still. His orange head twitched and jerked perpetually from side
45 to side in the most alarming fashion, and each twitch was accompanied by a little grunt that came out of his nostrils. He had been a soldier in the army in the Great War and that, of course, was how he had received his title. But
50 even small insects like us knew that 'Captain' was not a very exalted rank and only a man with little else to boast about would hang on to it in civilian life.

For a reason that I could never properly
55 understand Captain Hardcastle had it in for me from my very first day at St Peter's. Perhaps it was because he taught Latin and I was no good at it. Perhaps it was because already, at the age of nine, I was very nearly
60 as tall as he was, or even more likely, it was because I took an instant dislike to his giant orange moustache and he often caught me staring at it with what was probably a little sneer under the nose.

(from *Boy – Tales of Childhood* by Roald Dahl)

Glossary

brilliantine: an oily mixture to make men's hair shine and stay in place
tramlines: metal tracks along which buses driven by electricity run
walrus: an animal which has two long teeth which hang down
the Great War: the World War which took place from 1914–1918
a corrugated brow: eyebrows which were always joined together in a frown

2 Underline the correct alternatives.

a) Hardcastle had *red* / *black* / <u>*reddish-orange*</u> hair.

b) His hair was *dry* / *oily*.

c) His hair was *tidy* / *untidy*.

d) His moustache was *bushy* / *cut short* / *wavy*.

e) His face seemed *kind* / *cruel* / *clever*.

f) He was *overweight* / *strong* / *quite thin* / *very tall*.

3 Write *T* (for *True*) or *F* (for *False*) next to the following statements according to the text.

a) Hardcastle liked children. _____

b) He trusted other people too much. _____

c) He wasn't a relaxed person. _____

d) He had an important title. _____

e) Hardcastle disliked the writer. _____

f) The writer liked Hardcastle's appearance. _____

PRONUNCIATION

Words from the text

1 The following list gives the phonemic transcription of some words from the text. Write down the words, using the pronunciation chart on page 149 of the Students' Book to help you.

a) /streɪt/ _____straight_____

b) /ɪnsekt/ _____

c) /kəʊm/ _____

d) /dʒaɪənt/ _____

e) /bəʊst/ _____

f) /məstɑːʃ/ _____

2 Mark where the stress falls in the following words. Then use the dictionary to check your answers.

a) *head'master*   e) gymshoes

b) nailbrush   f) dangerous

c) football   g) perpetually

d) moustache

GRAMMAR

Form and function

Match the communicative functions (a–i) to the meaning expressed in the sentences in the dialogue below. In some cases there is more than one possibility.

a) ability   f) advice

b) asking about obligation   g) prohibition

c) offer / promise   h) agreement

d) suggestion   i) asking for

e) prediction   confirmation

'I can't ski very well.' (1 _a_)

'Neither can I.' (2 ___)

'Let's go for lessons on a dry ski slope before the holiday' (3 ___)

'Do we have to wear special clothes?' (4 ___)

'Well, if I were you I'd wear waterproofs, (5 ___) otherwise you'll probably get soaking wet.' (6 ___)

'I'm not allowed out in the evening while these exams are on (7 ___). It'll have to be weekends.'

'OK. I'll book a lesson for next weekend, then, (8 ___) shall I? (9 ___)'

Functional English ✗

Write what you would say in these situations.

a) You are late for dinner at someone's house. Apologise and give a reason.

_____

b) A friend of yours is unhappy in her job. Give advice.

_____

c) Invite somebody you like to go out for a drink.

_____

d) Ask your boss for permission to leave early.

_____

e) Ask a stranger in the street if they can tell you where the bank is.

_____

f) You can't go to your friend's party. Apologise and make an excuse.

_____

Verb forms and time

1   Write the name of the verb form given in *italics*.

a) We're *leaving* at six.   <u>*Present Continuous*</u>

b) When she *arrives* we'll go.   _____

c) *Have* you *finished* yet?   _____

d) I *used to* live in Rome.   _____

e) If I *had* time I'd do it.   _____

f) After he'*d told* me I had to sit down.

_____

g) She *may* phone later.   _____

h) I'*ve been living* here for two years.

_____

2   Match each verb form from Exercise 1 with the relevant heading below, depending on the time it refers to. Example:
We're leaving refers to future time so a) goes under *Future*.

1 Present   ___

2 Past seen from the present   ___ ___

3 Past   ___

4 Past seen from the past   ___

5 Future   <u>*a*</u> ___ ___ ___

Revision grammar

Look at the following sentences in which the grammatical errors have been underlined. Correct the errors.

a) I am the <u>most young</u> in my family and I <u>like very much to have older brothers and sisters.</u>

_____

b) When I <u>will leave</u> school I would like <u>going</u> to university <u>for to study</u> business.

_____

c) I didn't know whose book <u>was it</u>. Then I realised it was <u>her</u> so I have returned it to <u>she</u>.

_____

d) I haven't got <u>no luggages</u> but I have much books to carry.

_____

e) My money <u>stole</u> while I <u>travelling</u> on the bus.

_____

VOCABULARY

Plurals

Write down the plurals of the following words.

a) child   <u>*children*</u>   g) house   _____

b) baby   _____   h) tooth   _____

c) potato   _____   i) foot   _____

d) lady   _____   j) wife   _____

e) sheep   _____   k) bus   _____

f) mouse   _____   l) furniture   _____

Describing people

1   On a separate sheet of paper, copy the network below. Put the words from the box in the appropriate places on the network.

auburn   oval   vivacious   curly
twinkling   plump   shoulder-length
elderly   teenager   broad-shouldered
placid   shy   well-built   long-lashed
wide   middle-aged   glasses   freckles
skinny   toddler

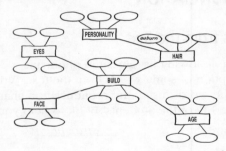

2   Make another copy of the network with the same headings. Put vocabulary from the reading text about Captain Hardcastle in the appropriate places. Example: hair – *ginger*

WRITING

Personal description

On a separate sheet of paper, write a description of somebody who was important to you in your childhood, e.g. a teacher, a relative, a first love. Include in your description information about:
– their physical appearance.
– their personality.
– the place they had in your life.

• Cruel to be kind? •

LISTENING

1 [■□ 2.1]   Listen to two extracts in which Pat is talking about her childhood and her own children's upbringing. Write *T* (for *True*) or *F* (for *False*) next to the following statements.

a) Pat's parents didn't use to have a car. _____

b) Pat doesn't find it easy to talk to her father. _____

c) Pat's children show affection to their father. _____

d) Pat feels that her parents didn't care about their children all the time. _____

e) She thinks she had a very good education. _____

f) Pat and John waited until they were older to have children. _____

g) They have two children. _____

h) The children are still at school. _____

2   Listen again to Extract 1. Write down three differences between Pat's upbringing and the way her own children were brought up.

a) _____

b) _____

c) _____

3   Listen again to Extract 2. Tick the following words or expressions which Pat thinks best describe either her husband or herself as parents.

a) caring _____

b) consistent _____

c) patient _____

d) mature _____

e) generous _____

f) worried about education _____

GRAMMAR

Review of the present

Change the verbs in brackets to either the Present Simple or the Present Continuous.

Richard is a househusband, which means that every day his wife (1 *go*) _____goes_____ off to work and (2 *leave*) _____ him at home to look after their two young children. Although the family (3 *live*) _____ in Oxford his wife (4 *work*) _____ in London this year so she (5 *not usually get back*) _____ home before 8 p.m. However, Richard (6 *think*) _____ the arrangement is a good idea. 'For the moment I (7 *still enjoy*) _____ the change in my lifestyle and I (8 *not need*) _____ to get the train to work every day, which is great! I (9 *also learn*) _____ lots of new things. For example, I now (10 *understand*) _____ how difficult it is to do the housework as well as look after two children.' This afternoon Richard (11 *want*) _____ to do some work on the book he (12 *write*) _____, but he (13 *not think*) _____ this is very likely. 'I (14 *find*) _____ it difficult to concentrate. Even when the baby is asleep I often (15 *feel*) _____ too tired to write anything.'

Habit in the past

Look at this extract and replace the Past Simple forms in *italics* with *used to* (+ base form) and/or *would* (+ base form). In some cases only one is possible. If the past forms cannot be replaced put a cross.

> I (1) *loved* living in a tropical climate. On a typical day I (2) *got up* early in the morning when it still (3) *felt* relatively cool, and (4) *walked* along the beach. Once I (5) *went* out in a boat for the day. I (6) *shopped* in the market for fish which I (7) *ate* at every meal. I (8) *did* most of my work early and in the afternoons I (9) *slept*. We (10) *had* a wonderful old house with big gardens full of tropical fruit.

1 *used to love* _____   6 _____
2 _____   7 _____
3 _____   8 _____
4 _____   9 _____
5 _____   10 _____

Used to (do) or *be used to (doing)*?

Underline the correct form of *used* in the sentences below and write the correct form of the verb in brackets.

a) I *used / am used* to (*spend*) _____ a lot of money on clothes and books but now I have children I can't afford it.

b) He's very nervous about the conference because he *didn't use / isn't used* to (*make*) _____ speeches.

c) She is old and frail now but when she was young she *used / was used* to (*be*) _____ a top gymnast.

d) My eyes keep watering because I *didn't use / am not used* to (*wear*) _____ contact lenses.

The definite article

Complete the following sentences with *the*. Leave a blank if the article is not needed.

a) Could you turn on _____ light, please?

b) Tom is learning to play _____ piano, did you know?

c) Children go to _____ school between the ages of five and sixteen.

d) My cousin has just joined _____ Navy.

e) Jill has _____ beautiful eyes.

f) We are thinking of going on holiday either to _____ Europe or _____ Far East.

g) We're going to have _____ dinner in _____ garden.

h) Many people think _____ old people are treated very badly in _____ Britain.

i) Tim is a strong believer in _____ love and _____ peace.

VOCABULARY

Prefixes

Complete the sentences below with prefixes from the box.

anti	mis	auto	sub	co	pre	ex	non

a) A pilot always has a _____-pilot to help him.

b) Famous people are often asked to write _____biographies about their life.

c) _____-packed food is useful for busy people who haven't got a lot of time to cook.

d) My _____-wife still lives in Panama with our son. We keep in regular contact.

e) The reason I didn't understand was that you _____pronounced the word *naughty*.

f) Do you mind if we go in a _____-smoking compartment? I'm trying to give up cigarettes.

g) Max has gone on an _____-war demonstration in protest about our involvement in the production of nuclear weapons.

h) We had to live in _____-zero temperatures.

Word building

Change the words in brackets to a verb, adjective or noun.

a) These streets are too narrow. They should (*wide*) _____*widen*_____ them.

b) Italian parents often treat their children with great (*tender*) _____.

c) One of the great (*attract*) _____ of this country is the mountains.

d) I didn't put any sugar in your tea. You may want to (*sweet*) _____ it yourself.

e) Do you know a doctor who (*special*) _____ in childcare?

f) The child was (*terror*) _____ when he saw the dog.

g) They got a lot of (*enjoyable*) _____ out of the film.

h) The shop assistant showed a lot of (*patient*) _____ with the difficult customer.

Compound nouns

Headache, seat belt and *egg-cup* are examples of compound nouns. Write down at least three examples of compound nouns using the words on the right as second words.

Check in your dictionary to see if they are written as one word, two words, or with a hyphen.

a) paper *notepaper* _____

b) machine _____

c) room _____

e) book _____

WRITING

Dictation

1 [🔊 2.2]   Listen to a short extract about Richard. Then listen again and write down what you hear on a separate sheet of paper.

2   Underline ten phrasal verbs in the text.

• TV or not TV? •

READING

Jeff's story

We thought that a computer would be the ideal gift for our three-year-old son because it would be educational. My husband, Jeff, brought one home and set it up on the table
5 in the living room.

Switching on the machine, Jeff started to play the space invaders game that came with it. I joined in, competing against him. It was good fun for half an hour but then I
10 grew bored and watched TV instead. However, Jeff remained glued to the screen for the whole evening, and the next day he stayed up until 2 a.m. From then on, first thing every morning he sat at the computer,
15 spooning cornflakes into his mouth while he played. At night I'd cook a meal and he'd eat it off his knees so he didn't have to stop his games. He stopped talking to me and our little boy, Owen, and he lost interest in
20 everything else. When he wasn't asleep or at work he played games. He'd stay up until 3 a.m., becoming exhausted but unable to tear himself away. He could hardly drag himself to work in the mornings. One day he
25 arrived home unexpectedly and said he'd lost his job. The factory manager had complained about his lateness and Jeff had walked out. He wasn't concerned that his family would have to survive on the dole.
30 Now he could play his computer games all day long without work getting in the way.

I struggled to run the household. Jeff didn't lift a finger to help, nor did he search for work. Yet before the computer came
35 he'd been so considerate. We survived on £77 a fortnight. Yet he thought nothing of blowing £20 – our weekly food bill – on a new game.

Jeff was like an alcoholic – an addict. Yet
40 there was no support group to turn to, no Computer Addicts Anonymous. I love my husband deeply. We've been married for ten years and I thought we'd be together forever. And he flatly refuses to believe he
45 has a problem.

(from *Take a Break*)

Lynda's story

I live with my family and I do things like sneaking down first in the morning to open their letters. I've even stolen letters I see sticking out of neighbours' letterboxes. My
5 family are sick of coming out of rooms and finding me standing by the door eavesdropping.

When I go to friends' houses I look through their personal belongings and if
10 ever I'm alone in a house I can't help myself looking in drawers and cupboards. I go through the wastepaper bins and I can spend hours hiding behind the curtains and watching what the neighbours are up to.
15 They're always complaining and my parents are at their wits' end.

I know it's irrational but I do it because I'm afraid something terrible will happen if I don't keep a check on people. Being
20 addicted to snooping isn't that unusual. I'm having behavioural therapy at the moment and my therapist has told me of one woman who would dig through her neighbours' rubbish at the council dump. At least I'm not
25 that bad.

(from *More!*)

1   Jeff and Lynda have different problems. Read their stories quickly and write down what the problems are.

Jeff: _____

Lynda: _____

2   Read Jeff's story again and underline the correct answer from the following alternatives.

a) The computer was a gift for *Julie / Jeff / Owen*.

b) Jeff played with the computer *at night / in the morning / both*.

c) Jeff *lost his job / walked out of his job*.

d) Jeff was *upset / not worried* about being out of work.

e) Jeff *admits / doesn't admit* he has a problem.

f) *There is / There isn't* an organisation to help people like Jeff.

g) Julie *has divorced / is still married to* Jeff.

3   Read Lynda's story again and complete the following sentences to make a list of the six things which Lynda does when she's 'snooping'.

a) She sneaks _____

_____

b) She steals _____

_____

c) She eavesdrops _____

_____

d) She looks through _____

_____

e) If she's alone in a house she _____

f) She hides behind _____

_____

4   Answer the following questions.

a) How do Lynda's parents feel about her addiction? _____

_____

b) What do the neighbours do? _____

_____

c) What is she doing about her problem?

_____

_____

Vocabulary in context

Tick the best definition of the words and expressions in **bold**.

Jeff's story

a) *Jeff remained **glued to** the screen* . . . (line 11)

  i)   He was physically incapable of moving. ____

  ii) He couldn't stop watching. _____

b) *He could hardly **drag himself** to work* . . . (lines 23 and 24)

  i)   He went to work reluctantly. _____

  ii) He found it difficult to walk to work. _____

c) *Jeff didn't **lift a finger** to help* . . . (line 33)

  i)   He didn't like using his hands. _____

  ii) He would make no effort. _____

d) *He thought nothing of **blowing** £20 on a new game.* (lines 36–38)

  i)   Wasting money extravagantly. _____

  ii) Winning money. _____

e) *He **flatly refuses** to believe he has a problem.* (lines 44 and 45)

  i)   He denies he has a problem. _____

  ii) He is bored with discussing his problem. ____

Lynda's story

f) *I do things like **sneaking** down first* . . . (lines 1 and 2)

  i)   Running. _____

  ii) Going quietly and secretly. _____

g) *My family are **sick of** coming out* . . . (line 5)

  i)   Ill. _____

  ii) Tired of. _____

h) *. . . watching **what** the neighbours **are up to**.* (line 14)

  i)   How far they have got. _____

  ii) What they are doing. _____

VOCABULARY

Entertainment

Complete the definitions below.

a) A large group of musicians is called an

o _ _ _ _ _ _ _.

b) A flute, a clarinet and a guitar are different
kinds of i _ _ _ _ _ _ _ _ _.

c) Actors perform on a s _ _ _ _.

d) The seats on the ground floor of a cinema or
theatre are called the s _ _ _ _ _.

e) Actors in a play or film are called the c _ _ _.

f) A 'popular' newspaper with small pages is
called a t _ _ _ _ _ _.

Intensifying adjectives

Match the adjectives in column A with the
stronger adjectives in column B.

A	B
a) big	1 filthy
b) sure	2 starving
c) surprising	3 furious
d) angry	4 huge
e) clever	5 appalling
f) bad	6 amazing
g) hungry	7 positive
h) dirty	8 brilliant

Adjectives and prepositions

Complete the sentences below with prepositions
from the box. Some words may be used more
than once.

for	of	in	at	with	on

a) I was appalled _____ his behaviour.

b) The cinema was full _____ people.

c) She was thrilled _____ her new toy.

d) Is Amy jealous _____ the new baby?

e) Pisa is famous _____ its leaning tower.

f) He's involved _____ all the discussions.

g) Are you keen _____ the idea?

h) I'm not at all interested _____ football.

GRAMMAR

Present, Present Perfect or Past?

1 Look at the news extracts below and change
the verbs in brackets to the simple or continuous
form of the Present, Present Perfect or Past. In
some cases, the order of the words may change.

Here is a summary of the news.

a) The Prime Minister (1 *just announce*) <u>has just
announced</u> that there will not be a January
election. He (2 *speak*) _____ at
the opening of Parliament a few minutes ago.
His speech (3 *still go on*) _____.

b) Police (1 *find*) _____ the toddler
who (2 *disappear*) _____ from her
home a week ago. Detectives in Oxford
(3 *question*) _____ people all
week in connection with the abduction but so
far no one (4 *charge*) _____.

c) The economic situation (1 *finally begin*)
_____ to improve, according to
figures which (2 *release*) _____
yesterday. Unemployment has also (3 *fall*)
_____ gradually over the last few
months and export figures (4 *reach*)
_____ their highest level last
month.

2 [🎵 3.1]   Listen to the news broadcast
and check your answers. Then check the Key
for any alternatives.

Duration

For each of the following sentences write a question and then an answer. You may need to change the verb.

a) James began working two hours ago. He's still working now.

   i) How long _has James been working?_

   ii) He's _been working for two hours._

b) I moved into my flat in 1984.

   i) How long _____?

   ii) I've _____.

c) He got the car five years ago and he's still got it.

   i) How long _____?

   ii) He's _____.

d) Anne left to travel round the world three months ago and she's still travelling.

   i) How long _____?

   ii) She's _____.

e) I started feeling ill last Monday and I still feel awful.

   i) How long _____?

   ii) I've _____.

Present Perfect Simple or Continuous?

Put the words in *italics* into the most appropriate form of the Present Perfect.

a) I (*work*) all afternoon and I'm fed up.

  I've been working all afternoon and I'm fed up.

b) I (*write*) six letters and one report but (*not finish yet*).

_____

c) I (*eat*) all day because I'm bored.

_____

d) I (*already eat*) five bars of chocolate and (*drink*) six cans of lemonade.

_____

e) She (*teach*) all over the world for the last fifteen years and now she (*decide*) to come home.

_____

PRONUNCIATION

Silent letters

[🔊 3.2]   Listen to the following words and cross out the consonant which is not pronounced.

a) is̸land

b) handsome

c) honest

d) thumb

e) knife

f) sandwich

g) receipt

h) bomb

i) autumn

j) doubt

k) knee

l) whisky

WRITING

Dictation

[🔊 3.3]   Listen to the recording and write the sentences. They include words which are often spelled wrongly.

a) _____

b) _____

c) _____

d) _____

e) _____

f) _____

g) _____

h) _____

• But I can't do without it! •

LISTENING

Before listening

1 Underline two of the following which are not card games.

poker pontoon chess roulette baccarat
snap draughts

2 Choose a word from the box to fit each of the definitions below. They all refer to gambling.

> stake jackpot token dealer winnings

a) The money you get when you win in gambling. _____

b) The largest amount of money to be won at cards. _____

c) Money that can be won or lost. _____

d) The person who gives out the cards. _____

e) A piece of metal, card or plastic used instead of money. _____

Listening

1 [📼 4.1] Listen to the first part of a radio programme about Las Vegas, and answer the questions below.

a) In which US state is Las Vegas?

_____

b) How much money is made there each year from gambling in casinos?

_____

c) What kinds of gambling take place at the airport?

_____

d) What is the population of Las Vegas?

_____

e) Name three typical buildings you can see in Las Vegas.

_____

f) What does much of the city look like?

_____

2 [📼 4.2] Listen to the second part of the radio programme, and underline the correct answers or complete the sentences below.

a) Caesars Palace describes itself as a *fantasy land / a theme casino*.

b) The gambling takes place _____ days a year.

c) People sometimes gamble more than _____ dollars.

d) The Alabaman woman is *not winning anything / keeps winning*.

e) The Alabaman couple once won _____ dollars from the machines.

f) A housewife from Detroit once won _____ _____ dollars.

g) She spent her money on _____

_____

h) Next to the Colorado River there is a gambling place for *older people / children*.

GRAMMAR

Sequence of tenses

Link the sentences to make one complete sentence that means the same. Change the base forms of the verbs in *italics* to the correct form and make any other changes that are necessary.

a) I (*get*) to the station. The train already (*leave*).
   When I <u>got to the station, the train had already left.</u>

b) Louise (*cook*) the lunch. Meanwhile children (*sleep*).
   While Louise _____

c) I (*do*) the shopping first. Afterwards, I (*go*) home.
   After I _____

d) I (*see*) the burglary. I immediately (*ring*) the police.
   When _____

e) I (*check into*) the hotel. Then I (*phone*) my boss at once.
   As soon as _____

f) Sarah (*do*) the ironing. She (*hear*) a loud noise outside.
   When _____

g) Sarah (*hear*) a loud noise. She (*go*) outside to investigate.
   When _____

Past Perfect Simple or Continuous?

Underline the correct verb forms.

a) He was taken to the police station because he
   had crashed / *had been crashing* into the car in front of him.

b) The reason he had an accident was that he
   had driven / *had been driving* 300 miles that day and was very tired.

c) I was angry with him because he *had forgotten* / *had been forgetting* to buy a present for the baby's birthday.

d) I *had shopped* / *had been shopping* that morning so I could have got something.

e) The year before I met Tom I *had been skiing* / *had skiied* and *had broken* / *had been breaking* my leg.

f) When he died he *had written* / *had been writing* his autobiography. He *had written* / *had been writing* about half of it.

Narrative forms

Change the verbs in brackets to the Past (Simple or Continuous) or the Past Perfect (Simple or Continuous). In some cases there may be more than one possibility.

a) While I (1 *play*) <u>was playing</u> football I (2 *hurt*) _____ my leg. However, until I (3 *see*) _____ the doctor I (4 *not realise*) _____ that I (5 *break*) _____ it quite badly.

b) The police (1 *go*) _____ to the bank after a neighbour (2 *phone*) _____ to tell them what (3 *happen*) _____. However, they (4 *discover*) _____ that the robbers (5 *escape*) _____ in a stolen car. They (6 *kill*) _____ one of the bank clerks as he (7 *try*) _____ to escape and the others (8 *lie*) _____ on the floor, with their hands above their heads.

c) Suddenly they (1 *hear*) _____ a strange noise and they (2 *look*) _____ at each other in terror. All evening they (3 *play cards*) _____ and (4 *watch*) _____ television without thinking of the 'ghost'. But now they (5 *begin*) _____ to wonder if what Lucy (6 *tell*) _____ them might be true after all.

VOCABULARY

Phrasal verbs

Look at the dictionary definitions of the phrasal verbs on the right. Then match the words in *italics* in the following sentences with the definitions.

a) The business has *got control of* another one now. _____take over_____

b) Joanna *is* really *like* her mother, isn't she? You would think they were twins. _____

c) I've *begun to play* chess – I really enjoy it.

_____

d) His charming manner really *deceived* her. In fact he was a dishonest person.

_____

e) I'm going to *have* a week's *holiday* from work.

_____

f) That dress is too big for me. I'll have to *make* the waist *narrower.* _____

g) Tony is brilliant at *imitating* the teacher.

_____

> **take after** sbdy.   to look or behave like (an older relative)
> **take** sbdy./sthg. ↔ **in**   1 [T] to receive into one's home; to provide lodgings for (a person)   2 to include   3 to make (clothes) narrower   4 to understand fully   5 to deceive
> **take off** [T]   1 [T] (**take** sthg. ↔ **off**) to remove (esp. clothes)   2 [I] (of a plane, etc.) to rise into the air at the beginning of a flight   3 [T] (**take** sbdy. ↔ **off**) *infml* to copy the speech or manners (of someone)   4 [T] (**take** sthg. **off**) to have a holiday from work
> **take** (sthg. ↔) **over**   to gain control over and responsibility for (something)
> **take** sbdy./sthg. ↔ **up**   1 to begin to spend time doing; interest oneself in   2 to ask about or take further action about

Common errors

Look at the following sentences in which the vocabulary errors have been underlined. Rewrite the sentences, correcting the errors.

a) I've <u>forgotten</u> my book in my room.

_____

b) I'm just going to go and <u>take</u> it here.

_____

c) She <u>lost</u> the train because she was late.

_____

d) Some of my class are going on a <u>travel</u> next month.

_____

e) Remember to <u>control</u> your work before handing it in.

_____

f) Marcela is <u>expecting</u> Nikos outside the gate.

_____

g) Next week I am going to <u>pass</u> the exam.

_____

Verbs and prepositions

Complete the sentences with the appropriate prepositions.

a) We complained _about_ the food because it was so awful.

b) I forgot my purse so I couldn't pay _____ the shopping.

c) I agree _____ you, but we must think carefully about it.

d) Does this book belong _____ you?

e) Did they succeed _____ climbing the mountain?

f) What are you thinking _____ ?

g) Try to concentrate _____ the lesson.

h) The man shouted _____ the little boy for walking on the grass.

i) It depends _____ the weather.

j) I was laughing _____ the joke which Tim told me.

Places

Match the following places with the names in the signs. Where do you go if you want to:

a) find a house? __3__

b) gamble? _____

c) buy old furniture? _____

d) have your eyes tested? _____

e) have your pet treated? _____

f) book a holiday? _____

g) have your clothes washed? _____

h) have your watch repaired? _____

1 **Premier Travel Agency**

3
Comins
Estate Agents

2 **Sketchley Laundry and Dry Cleaning**

4 **Andrews Optician's**

5 **The Linden Antique Shop**

6 **Veterinary Surgery**

7 **Amusement Arcade**

8 **P. Smith: Jeweller's**

WRITING

Linking expressions

1 Underline the correct alternatives.

a) I was feeling hungry _so_ / _because_ I stopped at a café.

b) I missed the plane. _Although_ / _However_, I caught another one.

c) _While_ / _Meanwhile_ Sue was talking to Pete there was a knock on the door.

d) I didn't go to bed until after three, _so_ / _that's why_ I'm very sleepy.

e) _Since_ / _Although_ it's raining I won't go for a run this evening.

f) I went to university _to_ / _for_ study philosophy.

2 Complete the sentences below in an appropriate way.

a) I have two parrots and some tropical fish as well as _____

b) Although Sue has lived in France for ten years _____

c) The business started losing a lot of money. As a result _____

d) As I was feeling very thirsty _____

e) I may go to Australia at the end of this year. However, _____

f) The weather's been very cold recently. That's why _____

g) A lot of people come to England to _____

h) Even though I'm not at all keen on seafood _____

• A rare breed •

READING

1   Read the article and write down:

a) one thing that is necessary if job-sharing is going to succeed.

_____

b) one advantage of job-sharing.

_____

c) one danger when job-sharing.

_____

2   Write *T* (for *True*) or *F* (for *False*) next to each of the statements.

a) Successful job-sharing is like a permanent relationship. _____

b) If one of them leaves the other will have to resign. _____

c) They would prefer to spend more time with their children. _____

d) Jane's home life has improved now that she isn't so tired in the evenings. _____

e) According to Sheila, men don't job-share because they can't afford to. _____

3   Write the questions asked when the journalist got back to the office.

a) What _____ ?
   She's short, fair and introverted.

b) Who _____ ?
   Jane is; it's on language and the elderly.

c) Are _____ ?
   Yes, they both have PhDs.

d) Would _____ ?
   Yes, she would but men still aren't keen on the idea.

Now job-sharing is catching on

Job-sharing is a little like marriage, according to Dr Jane Maxim. You have to like each other and trust each other, and it's probably better if the two of you have different temperaments. Her job-sharer, Dr Sheila Wirz, agrees: "Like marriage, once you get it right, you stick with it."

5   Sheila and Jane have a lesson for those who long to job-share: ask and you may get. They put up the idea to their superiors, presenting a convincing case and setting out costs and considerations. What is more, they used it to gain promotion and get a research grant. Their contract has been carefully worked out: for example, should one of
10   them wish to leave, the other will first be offered the job full-time, then either accept another sharer or resign.

Jane, short, fair and introverted, and Sheila, tall, dark and extroverted, are an unusual example of this growing trend towards working in partnership. First, they are both well qualified with PhDs,
15   and they share a high-level job: co-ordinator of the BSc degree course at the College of Speech Sciences, one grade down from Principal. They are in charge of two hundred undergraduates, teaching, taking part in clinical work and doing research.

Second, their reason for sharing is not, like most women, to have
20   more time to spend with their children – Jane has none and Sheila's are grown-up. Both simply want more time to pursue their outside interests. For Sheila this means, for example, being a Parliamentary wife – her husband, Andrew Rowe, is Conservative MP for mid-Kent. She is also involved in a publishing venture. "I like the business
25   buzz as well as the academic life," she confesses.

Jane is writing a book on language and the elderly. She adds: "My husband is a solicitor and specialises in company law. Now instead of both of us returning home exhausted, only he does and it makes for a better home life."
30   She would love him to job-share too, but it's a concept that hasn't yet taken off with men. Is this because men's self-image is more tied-up with their work-image? "Well, that's what feminists would argue, but I'm not sure that I totally agree," says Sheila. "It would be difficult for many families to survive if the breadwinner was only on half
35   salary."

"I think initially the college didn't like the idea because they felt we were not putting our careers first," recalls Sheila. In reality, they are very much "full-time types". In their first year they found each was doing the same number of lecturing hours as her full-time colleagues.
40   "You have to be very careful not to take on more than your half."

(from The Sunday Telegraph)

Glossary

PhD: Doctor of Philosophy (a university degree of very high rank)
BSc: Bachelor of Science (a first university degree in a science subject)
MP: Member of Parliament

GRAMMAR

Mixed question forms

Complete the questions, using the information given in brackets to help you.

a) A: _____ *Who likes* _____ jazz?

   B: Me. (*I like jazz*)

b) A: _____ the cinema with?

   B: No one. (*I went by myself*)

c) A: _____ your jacket?

   B: Argentina. (*I bought it in Argentina*)

d) A: _____ give me a lift?

   B: Me. (*I'll give you a lift*)

e) A: _____ a good time?

   B: Yes. (*I had a good time*)

f) A: _____ weigh?

   B: 14 kilos. (*It weighs 14 kilos*)

g) A: _____ the biggest pizza?

   B: Leo. (*Leo ate the biggest pizza*)

h) A: _____ clean your shoes?

   B: This afternoon. (*I'm going to clean my shoes this afternoon*)

i) A: _____ like?

   B: Very nice. (*Brian's very nice*)

j) A: _____ like?

   B: (*He's got curly hair*)

Less direct and reported questions

Complete the following sentences.

a) 'Does her husband speak Malay?'

   'Could you tell me *whether her husband speaks Malay?*'

b) 'Where's the nearest post office?'

   'Would you happen to know _____ _____ ?'

c) 'Did they find any oil in the desert?'

   'Have you any idea _____ ?'

d) 'How many symphonies did Mozart write?'

   'Do you know _____ ?'

e) 'Were you happy at school?'

   He asked me _____

f) 'How often does Mike go swimming?'

   She wanted to know _____

Question tags

1 Match the sentences in column A with the question tags in column B.

A	B
a) You speak Russian,	1 will you?
b) Don't be late,	2 did they?
c) I shouldn't have gone,	3 aren't I?
d) Nobody came,	4 would you?
e) I'm very lucky,	5 don't you?
f) You wouldn't tell her,	6 should I?

2 Complete the following with the correct question tag. In two cases, there is more than one possibility.

a) Mary spoke to him, *didn't she* ?

b) He's already been, _____ ?

c) Nothing happened, _____ ?

d) Hurry up, _____ ?

e) John'll help, _____ ?

f) You've no idea, _____ ?

g) I couldn't borrow this, _____ ?

Word order

Rewrite the following putting the words in the correct order. In some cases there is more than one possible answer.

a) me / a letter / wrote / she

   She wrote me a letter.

b) to answer / question / I / that / refuse

c) the rules / to / please / us / explain

d) to Mali / I'm flying / on Friday / home

e) themselves / at the party / enjoyed / very much / everyone

f) the police / the accident / have you reported / to / ?

g) for / you / the tickets / tomorrow / I'll pay / at 8 o'clock

VOCABULARY

Men and women

Write *M* (for *Male*), *F* (for *Female*) or *B* (for *Both*).

a) lord _____   h) lad _____

b) maternal _____   i) swimming trunks _____

c) model _____   j) niece _____

d) bridegroom _____   k) blouse _____

e) widower _____   l) go into labour _____

f) nun _____   m) pretty _____

g) mare _____   n) babysitter _____

Synonyms and antonyms

Find a synonym (a word that means the same or similar) and an antonym (a word that means the opposite) in the box for each of the adjectives below when they are used to describe people.

> obstinate nude excitable prosperous
> mean straightforward flexible calm brave
> cowardly insincere clothed hard up
> generous

	Synonym	**Antonym**
a) genuine	*straightforward*	*insincere*
b) stubborn	_____	_____
c) naked	_____	_____
d) tight-fisted	_____	_____
e) highly-strung	_____	_____
f) courageous	_____	_____
g) well-off	_____	_____

PRONUNCIATION

Question tags

[📼 5.1] Listen to the recording and tick the questions where the speaker is sure about the answer and is just checking.

a) It's still raining, isn't it? _____

b) Brazil beat Italy, didn't they? _____

c) The tickets are all gone, aren't they? _____

d) We should leave, shouldn't we? _____

e) You've eaten snails before, haven't you? _____

f) You'll be fifty next birthday, won't you? _____

WRITING

Small ads.

1 Which of the 'small ads' (advertisements) is:

a) advertising somewhere to live? _____

b) offering employment? _____

c) selling something? _____

1 • **MAGICIANS/COMEDIANS** wanted for new club mid June. Phone 081-232 0809 eves or wknds.

2 • **COUNTRY** cottage to rent for a month. Secluded location. 1½ hrs central Cardiff, mod. cons, 1 bed, CH, £450 pcm neg./£120 pw. Suit sgl. Tel 0222 211607 office hrs only

3 • **VOLVO 360 GLT 1987** 5dr, elec windows, s/roof, CD, VGC for year! £4,300 ono. Tel 0487 822655

2 Find abbreviations for the following:

a) per calendar month _____

b) or nearest offer _____

c) very good condition _____

d) modern conveniences _____

e) hours _____

f) per week _____

g) central heating _____

h) evenings _____

i) bedroom _____

3 On a separate sheet of paper, write a 'small ad.' for the following, using abbreviations where possible.

You want to let a large double room in your house in London, 10 minutes from Oxford Circus. It is suitable for a young couple but you don't want to let it to smokers. The room has central heating and costs £80 a week. You can be contacted during the weekends on 081-636 1555.

The perfect interview

LISTENING

1 These are extracts from an interview between a doctor and a patient. The patient has a back problem. Try to match the words and phrases in *italics* in column A with the phrases in column B without using a dictionary.

A

a) Have you had *treatment* . . . __4__

b) I took some *painkillers* . . . _____

c) . . . just *bruising*. _____

d) a *tendency to get* . . . _____

e) it *flares up* every so often . . . _____

f) getting your back *X-rayed* . . . _____

g) damage that you actually *sustained* . . . _____

h) stop it *incapacitating you* . . . _____

i) movements which *aggravate it* . . . _____

j) advisable not to *over-exert* myself _____

B

1 examined by means of photographs

2 likelihood of developing

3 get too much physical exercise

4 someone trying to make it better

5 marks left under the unbroken skin

6 medicine to stop it hurting

7 preventing you from doing things

8 suddenly gets painful

9 experienced

10 make it worse

2 [6.1] Listen to all three extracts from the interview and check your answers to Exercise 1. Then check the answers in your dictionary.

3 Listen again and complete the doctor's notes.

PATIENT'S RECORD CARD

DESCRIPTION OF PROBLEM

Pain in (1)_____ part of (2)_____. Feels like tightening of (3)_____. Pain goes down to top of (4)_____. Pain occurs when patient is (5)_____ or when (6)_____. Usually lasts for (7)_____.

CAUSE

Caused by (8)_____ a few years ago.

PREVIOUS TREATMENT

Taken (9)_____. Never had physiotherapy but done some (10)_____.

RECOMMENDED TREATMENT

Recommended an (11)_____ to check on possible (12)_____. Gave a course of (13)_____ and arranged for some (14)_____. Advised patient not to (15)_____.

VOCABULARY

Collocation

1   Underline the parts of the body that can go with the adjectives. In some cases there may be more than one answer.

a)   **swollen** *adj*   increased beyond its usual size

<u>finger</u> / tooth / <u>ankle</u>

b)   **sore** *adj*   painful or aching from wound, infection, or (of a muscle) hard use

hair / throat / lips

c)   **pulled** *adj*   stretched and damaged by using force

muscle / thigh

d)   **twisted** *adj*   (a joint or limb) hurt by pulling and turning it sharply

shin / knee / ankle / wrist

e)   **fractured** *adj*   cracked or broken (a bone)

cheek / skull / throat

2   Complete the sentences with prepositions from the box. One preposition is used twice.

> from   of   in   under   on

a) What time will I be operated _____ ?

b) I'm feeling very _____ the weather today.

c) How long have you suffered _____ these headaches?

d) I've got quite a bad pain _____ my chest.

e) Have you got a sick note _____ your doctor?

f) The athlete died _____ a heart attack.

Medical terms

Circle the odd one out. Use your dictionary if necessary.

a) optician, (bruise), surgeon, chiropodist

b) diet, ache, itch, injury, wound, allergy

c) infection, sickness, injection, disease, illness

d) recover, cure, remedy, heal, outbreak

e) insomnia, transplant, transfusion, operation

GRAMMAR

Obligation

1   Comment on the following situations using the modal in brackets in either the affirmative or the negative. Change the main verb or add a verb.

a) I haven't got tickets for the play but let's go anyway. (*should*)
   You <u>should phone to see if there are any</u> <u>tickets left.</u>

b) Gabrielle ran to catch the bus but it had already gone. (*need*)
   She _____

c) Your children are outside in the road! (*must*)
   Really! I _____

d) I usually leave my car unlocked at night. (*should*)
   Don't be an idiot! You _____

e) They've been together for six years but never married. (*need*)
   I suppose they feel they _____

f) Ian hasn't got a formal suit to wear to the dinner. (*have to*)
   In that case he _____

2   Underline the correct alternatives.

a) It's a terrible job. *I must / have to* work at the weekends.

b) I don't think you *should / must* wear a pink tie. The party's quite formal.

c) You *needn't / mustn't* bother to vote. The Conservatives have almost certainly won.

d) I do think Keith *mustn't / shouldn't* be so sensitive about what people say.

e) What a fool I was! I *needn't worry / needn't have worried*. Tracy was at home all the time.

f) You *mustn't / don't have to* keep your money in the bank but it's much safer.

Advice

Give different advice in the following situations.

a) Sally can't find the money to pay for a cup of coffee.

   i) Try *looking in your other pocket.*

   ii) You'd better _____

b) You are talking to a politician about traffic problems.

   i) I think you should _____

   ii) I would recommend that _____

c) Jeff is suffering from a nervous breakdown.

   i) Take my advice and _____

   ii) Try _____

d) Your friend's house is very old and needs renovating.

   i) If I were you _____

   ii) I would advise you _____

e) Peter got into a fight the last time he went to the disco.

   i) He'd better not _____

   ii) It's time he _____

PRONUNCIATION

Connected speech

1 [6.2]   Listen to the recording and write down the number of words you hear in each sentence. (Contracted words (e.g. *needn't*) count as two words.)

a) _8_

b) ____

c) ____

d) ____

e) ____

2   Listen again and complete the sentences.

a) _____ more wine.

b) _____ the bus.

c) Why _____?

d) What _____?

e) I think _____.

WRITING

Letter of application

Look at the job advertisement and an extract from John Maley's CV. On a separate sheet of paper, write John's letter of application to accompany his CV for the post of Teacher of Economics.

SUFFOLK COUNTY COUNCIL
Samuel Ward Upper School

TEACHER OF ECONOMICS
Required from January to cover maternity leave.
At least two years experience essential.

To apply please send letter of application and CV to:
    The Headteacher,
    Samuel Ward Upper School,
    Chalkstone Way,
    Haverhill,
    Suffolk CB9 0LD

CURRICULUM VITAE

PERSONAL
NAME:John Maley
ADDRESS:84 Summerfields,
  Colchester, Essex
TELEPHONE: 0206 444366
DATE OF BIRTH: 14th April,1967

EDUCATION
St Mary's High School 1978-85
University of Fenland 1985-88
Huntingdon College of
  Further Education   1988-89

QUALIFICATIONS
Economics B.A. II, ii
  (Fenland)
P.G.C.E. Distinction
  (Hunts C.F.E.)

WORK EXPERIENCE
The Barn School (11-18 year-
  olds)
South Normanton,
South Yorkshire
BY11 20PQ   1989-91

Crawlers, winkers, flashers

READING

You are going to read three extracts from a book on how to fly a plane.

1 Look at the sequence of pictures which shows the different stages of take-off. Match the words and phrases in the box to give captions to the pictures.

> reaching flying speed   turning into the wind
> climbing   taxying   reaching safety speed

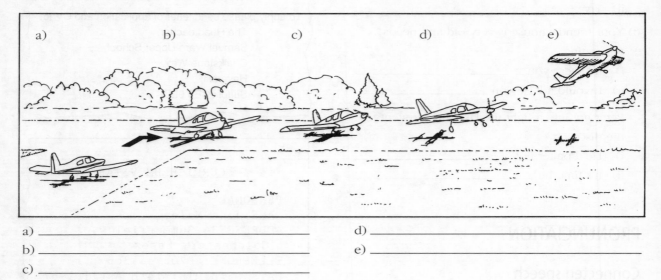

a)   _____
b)   _____
c)   _____
d)   _____
e)   _____

Now read the first extract and check your answers.

Taking off

First of all the aircraft is driven along the ground under the power of its engines to reach its correct position on the airfield. This is called taxying. When it reaches the end of the runway it is turned into the wind. The throttles are opened, the engines roar and the plane rapidly gains speed across the runway. As the ground speed increases so does the air speed, until the flying speed is reached. At that moment the plane can leave the ground and become airborne if the pilot slightly increases the 'angle of attack' (the angle at which the plane is inclined upwards or downwards).

The upward force of the air acting on the wings, and the plane's speed, have provided the necessary lift (that is the upward force of the air which makes the plane rise) to start it flying. After safety speed has been reached, the pilot can then ease back the control column (the hand-operated lever) to lift the nose of the machine further and so increase the rate of climb.

2 Read the first sentence of the second extract and tick the picture which indicates straight and level flight at a steady speed.

Level flight

For straight and level flight, lift must always equal the weight of the plane. If the pilot increases the speed, and does not alter the angle of attack the plane will rise. Therefore, to maintain level flight, the control column must be pushed forward to lower the nose and so decrease the angle of attack.

On the other hand, if the pilot reduces speed without altering the angle of attack the plane will lose height. The control column must therefore be pulled back to increase the angle of attack.

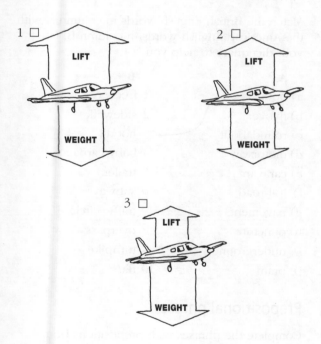

Now read the rest of the second extract and underline the correct alternatives.

a) The pilot has to bring the nose *up / down* when increasing speed to stop the plane from rising.

b) The pilot has to bring the nose *up / down* when decreasing speed to stop the plane from falling.

3 Read the third extract to complete the sentences below.

Landing

Landing demands flying the plane as slowly as possible without stalling (that is, without losing lift and stopping). When the plane approaches the ground, the plane has both forward and downward speed. The forward speed (in relation to the ground) which has been progressively decreased by cutting the engine power, is still further reduced by landing into the wind whenever possible.

At a point close to the ground, forward speed in relation to the air is reduced by completely closing the throttle. As the speed falls off, lift is maintained by raising the aircraft's nose slightly and progressively, thus increasing the angle of attack, and so keeping lift equal to the weight as the speed falls to its minimum for flying. Finally, as the forward speed continues to fall, a condition is reached when a plane is no longer moving at its flying speed. Ideally, this occurs at the moment when the wheels of the undercarriage touch the runway and the weight of the plane is transferred smoothly from the air to the ground.

a) If the plane is flown too slowly _____

b) The plane is landed into the wind whenever possible in order to _____

c) Lift is kept equal to weight by _____

d) The wheels of the plane should touch the runway when _____

GRAMMAR

Talking about the future

1   Cross out the forms which are *not* likely in the context. In some cases, there may be more than one possibility.

a) A: Have you decided what you *'re doing / ~~do~~ / 're going to do* next year?

  B: I *was going to / had hoped to / am going to* do a law degree but I decided against it.

b) A: *Will you bring / Shall you bring / Are you bringing* back that tape I lent you, please?

  B: Oh, sorry. I forgot. I *'m letting / 'll let* you have it this afternoon.

c) A: Find out what time *the film ends / the film's ending / the film's going to end.*

  B: Why? What *do you do / are you doing / are you going to do* afterwards?

d) A: I'm fed up. I *'m going / go* out for a walk.

  B: OK. I *'m seeing / 'll see* you later.

e) A: I hope you *are not forgetting / won't forget* my birthday.

  B: No. I*'m taking you / 'll take you* to the theatre. Remember?

2   Complete the sentences, using the correct future form in brackets.

a) A: Do you want a lift?

  B: Thank you but I think _____.
    (*'ll / Present Simple*)

b) A: Did you two ever get married?

  B: No, we _____ but then we decided not to. (*going to / 'll*)

c) A: Why haven't you made the cake yet?

  B: It's too early. I _____ this afternoon. (*going to / Present Simple*)

d) A: I must go and get the washing in.

  B: No, don't worry. I _____.
    (*'ll / Present Continuous*)

e) A: Can you come round tomorrow night?

  B: I'd love to but _____.
    (*'ll / Present Continuous*)

Future time expressions

Complete the following sentences, using suitable verbs in the correct tense.

a) Can you water the plants while we ____ away?

b) Before you _____ can you give me your key?

c) I _____ you the results as soon as I _____.

d) You won't be able to go out so much after the baby _____.

e) The weather's awful. Wait here until it _____ raining.

f) When we _____ the election, we _____ taxes, I promise.

VOCABULARY

American English

Match the British English words in column A with the American English words in column B. Use your dictionary to help you.

A	B
a) bonnet	1 freeway
b) flyover	2 sidewalk
c) roundabout	3 hood
d) motorway	4 baby carriage
e) caravan	5 trailer
f) toll road	6 subway
g) pavement	7 traffic circle
h) puncture	8 overpass
i) underground	9 turnpike
j) pram	10 flat

(a) bonnet → 3 hood)

Prepositional phrases

Complete the phrases with prepositions from the box.

at	by	on	in

a) *by* car

b) ____ foot

c) ____ bus

d) ____ sea

e) ____ air

f) ____ home

g) ____ board

h) ____ prison

Collocation

Complete the gaps with words from the box.

> give make change have take catch
> do turn

a) _____ *catch* _____ a cold / the bus / your breath / sight of

b) _____ the page / a corner / the handle / your nose up at

c) _____ progress / a fool of oneself / a noise

d) _____ a favour / the cooking / without / your best

e) _____ into / your mind / trains / gear

f) _____ your time / a seat / place

g) _____ advice / permission / the game away / evidence

h) _____ a good time / a baby / a look / a party

Forming adjectives and adverbs

Complete the sentences with adjectives or adverbs in the affirmative or the negative made from the words in brackets.

a) You're so boring and ___ *predictable* ___! (*predict*)

b) What a _____ house! (*delighted*)

c) She smiled and spoke to him _____. (*affection*)

d) We have had _____ rainfall this year. (*precedent*)

e) He was _____ rude. I'll never forgive him. (*necessary*)

f) Although he's a boxer he's not very _____. (*aggressor*)

g) Are you sure that snake isn't _____? (*poison*)

h) Steve looked tired and _____. (*shave*)

i) How _____ of you to forget my birthday again! (*thought*)

WRITING

Written style

[📼 7.1] Listen to the following story and, on a separate sheet of paper, rewrite it in a less colloquial style. Begin like this:

This year we were coming back from our holiday in Spain. The plane was very crowded with children everywhere and people . . .

'Yeah, well, let me tell you about when we came back from Spain this year. We had a real disaster. Or at least we nearly did, that's more to the point. OK. Just imagine it. The plane packed with everyone coming back from their holidays. Kids everywhere. People trying to get a drink. Stewards and stewardesses in a terrible mood. Chaos. When suddenly we . . . you know, the plane, like, well, it took an almighty dive. Nobody knew

what it could be. The weather was OK. No storm or anything. Then everyone was screaming. Even the cabin crew . . . Laugh? They were flat on their backs or on top of the passengers. A real sight I tell you! Bottles out of lockers. People grabbing hold of each other. I was white as a sheet. Absolutely terrified. Well, luckily – it seemed like hours – we pulled out of the dive. Eventually. And then we landed. Well, ten minutes later. And do you know what it was? You'll never guess. All the flight crew had fallen asleep. What about that, eh? Apparently, they'd all been on duty for twenty hours at a stretch. Well it's not right is it? Of course we really did some complaining at the airport. Threatened to write to the Prime Minister. Everything. Terrible really. Never again. It's boat for us next time.'

Anyone out there?

LISTENING

Before listening

> **Feb 20.** Lieutenant-Colonel John H. Glenn today became the first American to orbit the earth. His Mercury capsule, called Friendship 7, lifted off from Cape Canaveral at 9.47 a.m. local time and then splashed down in the Atlantic off Puerto Rico five hours later, after circling the earth three times.

1 Read the newspaper extract about something that happened in 1962 and tick the correct dictionary definition of the word in *italics*.

a) to *orbit* the earth:

   i)   travel away from _____

   ii) travel around the outside of _____

b) then *splashed down* in:

   i)   landed in the water of _____

   ii) crashed violently into _____

2 Complete items a) – c) on the incident report form.

(from *Longman Chronicle of the 20th Century*)

Listening

[▣ 8.1] Listen to the dialogue between astronaut John Glenn and Mission Control during the flight, in which there was a strange incident. Circle the correct alternatives on the incident report form.

Incident report form

Name of capsule:	a) _____
Name of astronaut:	b) _____
Date:	c) _____
Time:	d) `near dawn/midday/dusk/midnight`
Possible problem:	e) `spacecraft surrounded by insects/loose part/` `electrical storm`
Astronaut's first feelings:	f) `excited/frightened/disappointed`
Dangers:	g) `running out of fuel/overheating`
Astronaut's orders:	h) `reorbit/return to earth`
Astronaut given reason:	i) `yes/no`
Reaction to orders:	j) `excited/frightened/disappointed`

GRAMMAR

Future Continuous or Perfect?

Complete the sentences, using the verbs in brackets in the Future Continuous or the Future Perfect.

a) They say interest rates (*already rise*) __will__ ___already have risen___ to 10% by the end of the year.

b) Give her a ring. She (*get*) _____ back home by now.

c) Someone (*wait*) _____ for you there when you arrive.

d) 'Bye. We (*think*) _____ of you!

e) If we don't hurry, the film (*finish*) _____ before we get there!

f) I (*leave*) _____ at 7.00 exactly, so get in touch before then.

Future review

Complete the sentences using a verb from the box in a future form. In some cases there may be more than one possibility and you may need to add other words.

> clear up   carry   collapse   go   start   retire
> lie   give

a) *Will you give* _____ this watch to Kate, please?

b) We're going on holiday. This time tomorrow _____ in the sun.

c) That bag looks heavy. I _____ _____ for you.

d) You're 65, aren't you? When _____ _____?

e) By the time I get back I hope this mess

_____.

I don't want to see a thing.

f) Why don't we go to the concert? What time _____?

g) You've got a date with her, haven't you? Where _____?

h) According to the news, the Government

_____.

Complex sentences

Join the sentences below twice.
In (i) use one of the linking words from the box.
In (ii) use a participle construction.

> since   when   as soon as   although

a) We've booked a table at the restaurant. We might as well go.
   i) *Since we've booked a table at the restaurant, we might as well go.*
   ii) *Having booked a table at the restaurant, we might as well go.*

b) I can hear it clearly now. It still sounds awful.
   i) _____
   ii) _____

c) I get paid tomorrow. Then I'll give you the money.
   i) _____
   ii) On _____

d) I saw the film on TV. I thought it was old-fashioned.
   i) _____
   ii) _____

e) He's tall. He's always bumping his head.
   i) _____
   ii) _____

VOCABULARY

Words often confused

1   Complete the sentences with a word from the box.

> direction   path   directions   way

a) They strolled down the garden _____.

b) We were given _____ explaining how to get there.

c) Let's stop on the _____ to London.

d) Sam drove off in the _____ of Oxford.

2 Underline the correct alternatives.

a) Scientists have *discovered / invented* a new virus.

b) We live in a very *alone / lonely* house in the country.

c) The plants died through *lack / failure* of sunshine.

d) They offered a *prize / reward* for information about the stolen painting.

e) Will you *remember / remind* me to write to her?

f) I like the *identical / same* music as you.

Prepositions of time

Look at the museum opening times and then complete the dialogue with words from the box.

THE SYDNEY SCIENCE MUSEUM

Opening hours:
Monday-Friday: 10-1;
Mon, Tues, Thurs, Fri: 2-5.

until	to	before	in	on	for	at	by
between	from						

A: Yes, it's open every day (1)_____ Monday (2)_____ Friday.

B: There's a train that leaves (3)_____ two.

A: No, we'll have to go (4)_____ then. The museum's only open (5)_____ five. Besides, I have to be back home (6)_____ the time the museum closes because we're going out.

B: OK. Let's go (7)_____ the morning instead.

A: We'd better go early. It's closed (8)_____ one and two.

B: Really! How long's the place open (9)_____?

A: Only six hours a day. Oh, and only three hours (10)_____ Wednesday.

Idiomatic expressions

Complete the sentences with the expressions from the box. Use a dictionary to help you if necessary.

worlds apart   thinks the world
a world of good   dead to the world
the best of both worlds   means the world

a) I love my old car. It *means the world* to me.

b) We live in the country and have a flat in town. We have _____.

c) I tried to wake him up but he was _____.

d) Maggie may get fed up with you sometimes but really she _____ of you.

e) They don't like the same things. As people they're _____.

f) That medicine did me _____.

Compound adjectives

Make compound adjectives from the following phrases.

a) a boy who is ten years old
   a ten-year-old boy

b) a cat with green eyes
   _____

c) a hotel with three stars
   _____

d) a teacher with a strong mind
   _____

e) a woman who mainly uses her left hand
   _____

f) an actor with a big head
   _____

g) a run of three miles
   _____

h) bread that was made at home
   _____

WRITING

Abbreviations

Match the abbreviations in column A with the descriptions in column B. Refer to your dictionary to find out what the letters stand for if necessary.

A	B
a) VAT	1 member of the Royal Family
b) UK	2 common market organisation in Europe
c) EC	3 world organisation that helps children
d) IRA	4 tax on sold goods
e) NATO	5 illegal organisation in Ireland
f) OPEC	6 Great Britain and Northern Ireland
g) HRH	7 military organisation (a group of countries)
h) UNICEF	8 group of oil-producing countries

Dictation

1 [🔊 8.2]   Listen to the recording and complete the horoscope below.

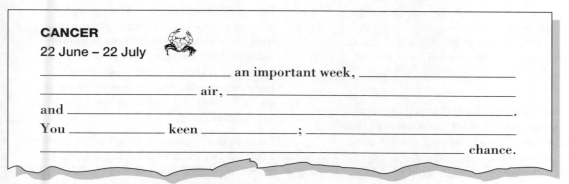

CANCER
22 June – 22 July

_____ an important week, _____
_____ air, _____
and _____.
You _____ keen _____; _____
_____ chance.

2 [🔊 8.3]   Listen to the recording of another horoscope.

a) On a separate sheet of paper, write down what you hear. When you hear a bleep sound leave a gap.

b) Fill in the gaps with words from the box.

patience   life   mood   advice   sake

LEO
23 July–22 Aug

3 [🔊 8.4]   Listen to the recording of the complete horoscope and check your answers.

Around the world

READING

With the aid of Garma's binoculars, we saw a flock of sheep trudging through the snow towards low ground. We were going to make it to Parayang! The sun was intense on the
5 snow and, to reduce the glare, I knotted my short plaits over the bridge of my nose, as Namgyal had done – far more successfully – with his. The other two lads had old snow goggles. My eyes were already stinging from
10 the blizzards and I would have given anything for Lobsang's goggles or Namgyal's longer pigtails. The snow cover got gradually thinner as we descended and by late afternoon we reached an inhabited nomad's
15 camp. There were real, live mongrel dogs snapping at our feet, sheep bleating, old women with toothless grins. Even a stream which wasn't a solid road of ice. Granted, it wasn't Parayang, but it sure felt like
20 Paradise! . . .

We met up with a flock of sheep and two shepherds and followed them towards their distant camp. It took another three hours, but it felt so good to be alive. I scarcely
25 noticed the pains which begged to tell me otherwise. A half-dozen ragamuffin children came out to welcome us and lead us proudly to their parents' camp. The tea tasted better than ever; the meat stew fresher, and to
30 round off the delicious feast, lashings of warm yogurt were served. Ah, angel's food. Blissfully satisfied, I crawled inside my sleeping bag and nestled down by the glowing embers. I closed my stinging eyes
35 and listened to the happy sound of the family. In the dead of night I woke in a pool of sweat. My eyeballs felt as if they were on fire. I fumbled blindly with the zip on my sleeping bag, trying to get some ventilation.
40 Someone had covered me in at least a dozen thick sheepskins. I tossed them off, and lay back again, panting. I couldn't see a thing. Snow-blindness. The dreaded ailment of

foolhardy mountaineers. The pain was
45 excruciating. I cried silently, continuously, until the stirring sounds of my host family intimated the dawning of a new day. Someone asked me what was wrong. *"Nga-rang mig mindu. Mig-chu mung bu mung
50 bu."* Literally, "I haven't got any eyes. Many, many tears."

I was at the lowest ebb imaginable. Suddenly I started to feel little prickling sensations about my midriff. I scratched the flesh thinly
55 covering my rib cage. It felt like a page of braille. Fleas! The sheepskins added to my bedding had left my sleeping bag infested with parasites. I scratched and I cried, and the tears made my eyes hurt even more.
60 Someone passed a cup of hot tea into my hands. I didn't bother to thank them. Revolting Tibetan tea. All the romance of being a nomad was wrenched from me.

(from *Tibet – A Woman's Trek Across a Mysterious Land* by Sorrel Wilby)

Glossary

plaits/pigtails: lengths of twisted hair
ragamuffin: dirty, young children with torn clothes
angel's food: beautiful food
foolhardy: foolish
rib cage: the bones protecting the lungs
braille: a form of printing for blind people

1 Read the text opposite about a long journey through Tibet by an Australian photojournalist and write a sentence for each of the items below to explain why they were significant to the writer. Use a dictionary to help you if necessary.

a) a flock of sheep *When they saw the sheep they knew they were getting near where they wanted to go.*

b) goggles _____

_____

c) sheepskins _____

_____

2 Answer the following questions.

a) Why would Sorrel have *given anything for . . . Namgyal's longer pigtails*? (lines 11 and 12)

_____

b) Why do you think the nomads' camp *felt like Paradise*? (lines 19 and 20)

_____

c) Why did Sorrel wake in *a pool of sweat*? (lines 36 and 37)

_____

Vocabulary in context

1 Find these phrases in the text and tick the best definition.

a) *snapping at our feet* (line 16)
   i)   trying to bite our legs _____
   ii) getting injured _____

b) *begged to tell me otherwise* (lines 25 and 26)
   i)   suggested that I should go to the doctor
   _____
   ii) suggested that life was not so good _____

c) *nestled down by the glowing embers* (line 33)
   i)   lay down next to the fire _____
   ii) tried to see what was around me _____

d) *fumbled blindly with* (line 38)
   i)   quickly opened _____
   ii) in the dark I tried to open _____

e) *lowest ebb imaginable* (line 52)
   i)   as depressed as it is possible to be _____
   ii) far end of the room _____

2 Write down a word or phrase with a similar meaning from the text. Use a dictionary to help if necessary.

a) walking with heavy steps (line 2) _*trudging*_

b) a large amount (line 30) _____

c) threw vigorously (line 41) _____

d) breathing quickly (line 42) _____

e) extremely bad (line 45) _____

f) taken violently (line 63) _____

GRAMMAR

Review of the article

Complete the following text with *a/an* or *the*. Leave a blank if no article is required.

a) Last night, _____ man was _____ victim of _____ violent attack. _____ identity of _____ man is being kept secret.

b) Put _____ baby back to _____ bed, turn off _____ light and go to _____ sleep.

c) I think that _____ friends, _____ peace of mind and _____ good job are _____ most important things in _____ life.

d) We always have _____ lamb for _____ lunch on Sundays. Would you like _____ egg on _____ toast if I get it for you?

e) When I arrived in _____ England, I bought a copy of _____ *Independent*, _____ typical British newspaper.

f) This morning I got in _____ taxi and went to _____ National Gallery in _____ Trafalgar Square.

g) I think _____ English are very arrogant, particularly _____ rich.

h) So you left _____ school at 16, went to _____ university two years later and got _____ degree in _____ economics.

i) Where did you say _____ university was?

j) This morning she did _____ shopping, went to _____ doctor and then went to _____ work.

Could / (was/were) able to / managed to

Underline the correct alternatives.

a) I *finally managed to / could finally* find what I was looking for.

b) They didn't want to go out but we *could / were able to* talk them into it.

c) When Pete was five he *could / managed to* speak four languages.

d) Gill had had a bad accident and *didn't manage to / wasn't able to* walk for a long time.

e) *Could you / Did you manage to* smell something burning just then?

f) I *was able to / could* get a ticket for the opera yesterday.

g) In the old days you *managed to / were able to* buy a house for less than £5,000.

Used for

Write down what each of the following objects is used for.

a) *It's used for opening tins.* _____

b) _____

c) _____

d) _____

e) _____

As/like

Tick the sentences in which *as* or *like* are used correctly.

a) Martin's a doctor, like Jim. _____

b) I once had a full-time job like a bricklayer. _____

c) Stop talking as my mother. You're my sister. _____

d) That car of yours is like a bus! _____

e) She spent ten years as Prime Minister. _____

f) I hate days as this. _____

g) I'll do like I like! _____

h) That soup tastes like dishwater. _____

WRITING

Sounds and spelling

1 Complete each of the following words with the letters which make the sound in brackets.

a) (/iː/) bel _ie_ ve _____ch   bl_____d
   c_____ling   p_____ple

b) (/f/) rou_____   to_____ee   _____otograph
   ha_____

c) (/eə/) ch_____   th_____   pr_____   r_____
   p_____

d) (/dʒ/) ba_____   _____oke   sol_____er
   ur_____

2 Write down the British-English spelling for these words with American spelling.

a) labor   _labour_____

b) center   _____

c) check book   _____

d) analyze   _____

e) jewelry   _____

f) catalog   _____

g) traveler   _____

h) pajamas   _____

VOCABULARY

Phrasal verbs

1   Put the words in the correct order to make sentences. The phrasal verbs are given in *italics*. In some cases more than one order may be possible.

a) *up* / prices / last year / *went* / a lot
   <u>Prices went up a lot last year.</u>

b) outside / *off* / a bomb / our hotel / *went*
   _____

c) *tell* / don't / *off* / me / please
   _____

d) the company / how long / *up* / will it take us / *to set*
   _____

e) could / it / *over* / *talk* / we / I wish
   _____

2   Read this extract from a story and rewrite the phrases in *italics* using one of the phrasal verbs in the box.

> see off   run away   pick up   call for
> go back   fed up with   set off for   go away
> go round   make for

I was *tired of* (1) ___<u>fed up with</u>___ living in that hot, polluted city. I decided to *leave* (2) _____ and do something different with my life, maybe *return* (3) _____ home and see my family. That evening I packed my bags and phoned my old friend Miguel to say goodbye. He was very upset and asked me to *pay him a visit* (4) _____ and *collect him* (5) _____ because he wanted to *come and say goodbye to me* (6) _____ at the airport. I packed my things, *phoned and asked for* (7) _____ a taxi and *began the journey to* (8) _____ his house. Why was I seeing old friends when I wanted to *escape* (9) _____ and leave this place forever? What a fool I was! I told the driver to change direction and *go directly to* (10) _____ the airport. To my surprise I couldn't control my tears.

Animals

1   Match the phrases in column A with the words in column B.

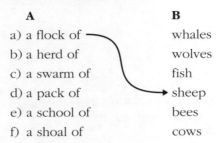

A	B
a) a flock of	whales
b) a herd of	wolves
c) a swarm of	fish
d) a pack of	sheep
e) a school of	bees
f) a shoal of	cows

2   Complete the gaps by matching the animals in the box with the sounds below.

> parrots   cows   mice   snakes   dogs   sheep
> monkeys   lions   horses

a) _____<u>sheep</u>_____ bleat
b) _____ moo
c) _____ neigh
d) _____ bark
e) _____ chatter
f) _____ hiss
g) _____ roar
h) _____ squawk
i) _____ squeak

Revision

READING

1   Look at the titles below. Read the 'Strange Stories' and match them with the titles.

a) **Close Shave**

b) *Ants in their pants*

c) **Chargeable call**

d) **Roaring success**

e) **Excuses, Excuses**

1

In Rochester, New York, Percy C Washington shot and killed Fannie Watson, 70, as she emerged from a Mother's Day church service. He had apparently mistaken her for his estranged wife Corene. "I meant to kill my wife, but I forgot my glasses," he said.

2   Wealthy Brazilians, exasperated by the phenomenal increase in crimes committed by their poorer compatriots, have taken to keeping lions to guard their exclusive homes. In one expensive apartment block, after a lion virtually ate a burglar alive, break-ins dropped from fifteen incidents a month to none.

3   William Mitcheson of Atlanta, Georgia, is the proprietor of America's only Ant Circus. His travelling exhibition of trained insects features such attractions as ant trapeze artists and tightrope walkers, and ants that dance and ride tiny bicycles. Visitors are issued with powerful magnifying glasses. Mitcheson, who spends several months training each performer, says the most difficult thing is to dress them in their clown costumes without squashing them.

4   In Annapolis, Maryland, a man was charged with stealing a car telephone. After discovering it was missing, the owner, Paula Thistle, dialled the number of the stolen phone, told the man who answered that she was lonely, and organised a date – but omitted to tell him that she would be chaperoned by the police, who arrested him when he showed up.

5   Benjamin Carnesoltas, 36, was convicted of slashing a prison officer at Lee's Summit, Missouri, with a razor blade. The fact that the weapon was not found did not deter the jury, to whom it was explained that Carnesoltas, a circus performer who could swallow and regurgitate objects at will, had gulped it down.

a) _____   b) _____   c) _____   d) _____
e) _____

2   All the stories above are true, except for one. Which do you think is the invented one? (Look at the last page of the book for the answer.)

3   Write *T* (for *True*) or *F* (for *False*) next to the following statements, according to the stories.

a) Percy C Washington killed his wife by mistake. _____

b) He was short-sighted. _____

c) Lions are kept as family pets in Brazil. _____

d) Keeping lions has stopped the break-ins. _____

e) There are lots of ant circuses in America. _____

f) People who go to the ant circus have to take magnifying glasses. _____

g) Paula Thistle helped to arrest the thief who stole her telephone. _____

h) Benjamin Carnesoltas was found guilty, although the weapon was not found. _____

GRAMMAR

Present, Present Perfect or Past?

Read the text below and underline the most appropriate verb form.

Until they (1) *broadcast* / *were broadcasting* the story of her life on TV no one (2) *heard* / *had heard* of Hannah Hauxwell. However, now she (3) *becomes* / *has become* a household name. She (4) *used to live* / *would live* seven miles from the nearest road, without any electricity or running water, and in the winter she was cut off if it (5) *snowed* / *was snowing* heavily. Her friends, who (6) *had been worrying* / *were worrying* about her for a long time, were very relieved when she finally (7) *decided* / *was deciding* to move. Last year TV viewers (8) *saw* / *had seen* her deep emotion at leaving the farm where she (9) *had been living* / *lives* for more than 30 years. Since then she (10) *bought* / *has bought* a cottage in a new village, where she (11) *has made* / *makes* new friends and where she regularly (12) *attends* / *is attending* the local church. She (13) *has just finished* / *just finished* her autobiography and last year she (14) *appeared* / *has appeared* on TV twice. At the moment she (15) *is writing* / *writes* another book about her life.

Question forms

Write questions using the cues below.

a) A: Who / Ruth / usually play / tennis / with?
       Who does Ruth usually play tennis with?
   B: Someone from work, I think.

b) A: How much / the Managing Director / earn?
       _____
   B: Over £40,000.

c) A: Which wild animals / not eat / meat?
       _____
   B: Elephants and rabbits, for example.

d) A: What / your steak / like?
       _____
   B: It's quite good, actually.

e) A: Can you tell me / where / bank / be?
       _____
   B: Yes, it's over there on the right.

f) A: Whose / be / that car?
       _____
   B: It's Adrian's.

Modals of obligation

Rewrite the sentences below in the present or the past, using the modals from the box.

mustn't   needn't   have to   must   should

a) They said you can't go in unless you pay.
   You ___*have to pay*___ if you go in.

b) It's important to phone him now. Go on!
   You _____ him.

c) It wasn't necessary to leave a tip.
   You _____ a tip.

d) You're not allowed to use dictionaries in the exam.
   You _____ dictionaries in the exam.

e) If I were you, I think I'd buy that house.
   You _____ that house.

f) It isn't necessary to buy him a present!
   You _____ him a present.

g) When I was a child I was made to eat cheese.
   I _____ cheese when I was a child.

Future forms

Underline the most appropriate form of the future below.

a) A: Are you feeling OK? You look as if you *are going to / will* faint.

  B: Yes, I suddenly feel a bit odd. I think I *'m going to / 'll* sit down for a minute, if you don't mind.

b) A: What do you think you *are doing / will be doing* this time next year?

  B: Well, by next March I *'ll finish / 'll have finished* my exams and I expect I *'m going to be / 'll be* on a hot beach somewhere.

c) A: When you go into town, *will you go / will you be going* anywhere near the bank, by any chance?

  B: Well, actually, I *'m going / 'll go* to the post office, which is next door.

d) A: When *will you have finished / are you finishing* reading that book?

  B: This evening I hope. I *'ll / am going to* pass it on to you.

VOCABULARY

Word building

Complete the sentences with a positive or negative form of the word in brackets.

a) At my school we had very little _____. (*free*)

b) Although many children enjoy them, for others schooldays can be a time of great _____. (*happy*)

c) The _____ of oil was very important for the country. (*discover*)

d) My skirts are too short. I'll have to _____ them. (*long*)

e) It takes a lot of _____ to play that game. (*patient*)

f) Sometimes he says things which are really _____ and which upset her. (*think*)

Prepositions

Complete the sentences below with an appropriate preposition.

a) When I take my holidays depends _____ my exam results.

b) I'm absolutely thrilled _____ my new car.

c) His brother's really keen _____ sport.

d) Have you ever suffered _____ migraines?

e) I'm afraid we'll have to operate _____ his leg.

f) This country is famous _____ its wine.

Phrasal verbs

Write down phrasal verbs from the box which correspond to the words in *italics*.

```
take up   see off   go up   go off   tell off
set up
```

a) The bomb *exploded* in the middle of a shop.
  ___went off___

b) Prices have *increased* a lot. _____

c) James has gone to the airport to *say goodbye* to his girlfriend. _____

d) My husband has decided to *start* a company. _____

e) The mother *spoke angrily* to her daughter, because she was being naughty. _____

f) A friend of mine has *started learning about* flower arranging. _____

Definitions

Complete the word for each definition.

a) You book a holiday from this person. (*n*)
  t _ _ _ _ _ _ _ _ _ _

b) Someone who won't change their mind is this. (*adj*) s_ _ _ _ _ _ _

c) Someone who is not brave is this. (*adj*)
  c _ _ _ _ _ _ _

d) *Sidewalk* is the American word for this. (*n*)
  p _ _ _ _ _ _ _

e) A group of sheep. (*n*) f _ _ _ _

f) Very sure. (*adj*) p _ _ _ _ _ _ _

g) Actors perform on it. (*n*) s _ _ _ _

PRONUNCIATION

Dictation

1 [📼 10.1]   Listen to the recording and write down in the boxes the word(s) which are stressed in each sentence.

a) _____ driving _____ train ?

b) _____ ☐ _____ ☐ ?

c) _____ ☐ _____ ☐ .

d) _____ ☐ _____ ☐ _____ .

e) _____ ☐ _____ ☐ .

f) _____ ☐ ?

2   Write down the other words in the sentences, then listen again to check if you were correct.

WRITING

Review of linking expressions

Complete the two stories below with linking expressions from the boxes.

afterwards   although   while   however   so

1 One snowy night, (a) _____ a family was driving down the motorway they noticed a dog in the road, (b) _____ they started to slow down. (c) _____, when they stopped they found that the dog had disappeared. (d) _____, someone told them that this part of the motorway was famous for a 'ghost dog'. Unfortunately, (e) _____ they went down that motorway many more times, they never saw it again.

as   as a result   meanwhile   but   when   because

2 (a) _____ I was 14 I had an 'out-of-body' experience. (b) _____ I was talking to my friends outside a shop, a mist suddenly came down. I thought this was very strange (c) _____ it was a very clear day, (d) _____ none of my friends seemed to notice. Suddenly, I found myself up in the air, looking down on my friends. (e) _____ they continued chatting to each other as if nothing had happened. (f) _____ of this experience I have always believed in the supernatural.

Scoop or snoop?

READING

The shocking case that shamed a nation

It was called 'The Crime of the Century'. Certainly there can have been no more bizarre case than the disappearance in the Australian Outback of tiny Azaria Chamberlain.

During a cool spring night in 1980, on a campsite at the famous Ayers Rock in the very heart of Australia, a baby disappeared. Was nine-week-old baby Azaria abducted by a dingo – an Australian wild dog – as her distraught mother maintained? Or did Lindy Chamberlain commit foul murder?

The case came to obsess a nation and triggered a media witch hunt that lasted for more than five years.

Azaria's body was never found, but her parents, Lindy and Michael, who were both deeply religious, were tried by rumour, suspicion and religious intolerance. Neither of them presented themselves well to the media, where they came over as unemotional and uncaring.

In a court of law Lindy was found guilty of murder. But with no body, no motive, no weapon and no clear evidence, why did an entire nation decide that a happily-married couple had killed their baby daughter?

The extraordinary real-life story and subsequent court-case is told in the film *A Cry in the Dark*, starring Meryl Streep and Sam Neill.

The director, Schepisi, said 'I came to realise this was a story of public perception versus private reality. The public's impressions of others are often incredibly wrong, on all sorts of levels. Here media misinformation and wrong impressions kept refuelling each other. A whole nation was playing pass-the-gossip: no wonder everyone was getting it wrong. Eventually it brought about a kind of group emotional madness.'

At the time of filming Lindy was still in prison, serving a life sentence for a murder she insisted had never occurred. (In 1986 she was freed, after serving three and a half years and in 1988 she was exonerated.)

While filming on location in Australia the tabloid press began to give Streep and Neill a taste of what the Chamberlains had gone through.

Just like the reports of the original Chamberlain case, wild stories circulated about the two stars, which bore little resemblance to fact.

Of *A Cry in the Dark* the producer, Verity Lambert, says 'I hope this is going to make other societies look at themselves and say "That could happen here: it could happen to anyone. It could have happened to me." There was the fact that it happened at Ayers Rock, where a multi-million-dollar complex of hotels was about to be built. I'm not implying that people said "We've got to find a murderer," but there was a subconscious feeling that it would be better if there weren't animals in the middle of the desert that ate children. Many people still believe that dingoes are lovely puppies. They forget there are no cans of dog food lying around the desert and so they have to eat live animals to survive. To a dingo, a baby is no different from a rabbit.'

Another aspect is that ordinary people need titillation. There's a desire to find evil in things, which is often exploited by the press. I think Lindy was tried by the press, but the public gets the newspapers it deserves. In the West we live in a media-driven society. We form opinions from newspapers, from how things are presented to us on television, and we make judgements on people perhaps thirty seconds after meeting them, depending on how they present themselves. It's wrong, but it's part of living in this society.'

(from *Flicks*)

Key

Unit 1

READING

1

Picture 2

2

b) oily   c) tidy   d) bushy; wavy   e) cruel
f) strong; quite thin

3

a) False   b) False   c) True   d) False   e) True   f) False

PRONUNCIATION

Words from the text

1

b) insect   c) comb   d) giant   e) boast   f) moustache

2

b) 'nailbrush   c) 'football   d) mous'tache
e) 'gymshoes   f) 'dangerous   g) per'petually

GRAMMAR

Form and function

2h)   3d)   4b)   5f)   6e)   7g)   8c)   9i)

Functional English

Examples:
a) I'm terribly sorry. I missed the bus.
b) If I were you, I'd look for another job.
c) Do you fancy going out for a drink?
d) Would you mind if I left early, please?
e) Excuse me. Do you know where the bank is, please?
f) I'm afraid I can't come to your party as I have to go away
   that weekend. I'm very sorry.

Verb forms and time

1

b) Present Simple   f) Past Perfect
c) Present Perfect   g) *may* (modal) + base form
d) *used to + base form*   h) Present Perfect Continuous
e) Past Simple

2

1 e)   2 c); h)   3 d)   4 f)   5 b); g); (e)

Revision grammar

a) I am *the youngest* in my family and I *like having older
   brothers and sisters very much.*
b) When I *leave* school I would like *to go* to university *to
   study* business.
c) I didn't know whose book *it was*. Then I realised it was
   hers so I have returned it to *her.*
d) I haven't got *any luggage* but I have *a lot of / lots of*
   books to carry.
e) My money *was stolen* while I *was travelling* on the bus.

VOCABULARY

Plurals

b) babies   c) potatoes   d) ladies   e) sheep
f) mice   g) houses   h) teeth   i) feet   j) wives
k) buses   l) furniture

Describing people

1

To complete the network:
Eyes: twinkling; long-lashed; wide; glasses
Personality: vivacious; placid; shy
Hair: auburn; curly; shoulder-length
Build: plump; broad-shouldered; well-built; skinny
Face: oval; freckles
Age: elderly; teenager; middle-aged; toddler

2

Examples:
Build: slim; wiry; thin legs
Personality: savage; insecure
Hair: ginger; dark vermilion; greasy
Face: moustache; inflamed; savage; corrugated brow

Unit 2

LISTENING

1

a) False   b) True   c) True   d) True   e) False   f) False
g) True   h) False

2

Examples:
a) Pat never had parties, but her children did.
b) She took much more interest in her children's
   upbringing.
c) Her husband was much more involved in the children's
   upbringing.
d) Pat and her husband have an affectionate, informal
   relationship with their children.

3

Best description:
a) caring   b) consistent   f) worried about education

GRAMMAR

Review of the present

2 leaves   9 am also learning
3 live   10 understand
4 is working   11 wants
5 doesn't usually get back 12 is writing
6 thinks   13 doesn't think
7 am still enjoying   14 find / am finding
8 don't need   15 feel

Habit in the past

2 used to get up / would get up
3 used to feel / would feel
4 used to walk / would walk
5 X
6 used to shop / would shop
7 used to eat / would eat
8 used to do / would do
9 used to sleep / would sleep
10 used to have

Used to (do) or *be used to (doing)?*

a) used to spend
b) isn't used to making
c) used to be
d) am not used to wearing

The definite article

a) the   b) the   c) –   d) the   e) –   f) – . . . the
g) – . . . the   h) – . . . –   i) – . . . –

VOCABULARY

Prefixes

a) co-pilot   e) mispronounced
b) autobiographies   f) non-smoking
c) pre-packed   g) anti-war
d) ex-wife   h) sub-zero

Word building

b) tenderness   f) terrified
c) attractions   g) enjoyment
d) sweeten   h) patience
e) specialises

Compound nouns

Examples:
a) newspaper; toilet paper; writing paper; wallpaper
b) washing machine; sewing machine; coffee machine
c) bedroom; spare room; bathroom; meeting room
d) phone book; notebook; exercise book; reading book;
   recipe book.

WRITING

Dictation

After Richard had finished <u>tidying up</u> the kitchen, he <u>looked through</u> the cupboard to see what he needed to get at the shops. He noticed they had <u>run out of</u> sugar, tinned tomatoes and coffee so he <u>wrote</u> this <u>down</u>. He then <u>threw out</u> the rubbish, <u>filled up</u> the dishwasher and <u>switched</u> it <u>on</u>, emptied the washing machine and <u>hung</u> the clothes <u>up</u> outside. Then he <u>cleared up</u> the children's mess and <u>poured</u> himself <u>out</u> a cup of tea.

Unit 3

READING

1
Jeff: He is addicted to computers.
Lynda: She is addicted to snooping.

2
a) Owen
b) both
c) walked out of his job
d) not worried
e) doesn't admit
f) There isn't
g) is still married to

3
a) She sneaks down first in the morning to open her family's letters.
b) She steals neighbours' letters out of their letterboxes.
c) She eavesdrops on her family.
d) She looks through her friends' personal belongings.
e) If she's alone in a house she looks in drawers, cupboards and wastepaper bins.
f) She hides behind the curtains and watches the neighbours.

4
a) They are sick of it, and at their wits' end.
b) They complain.
c) She's having therapy.

Vocabulary in context

Jeff's story
a) ii   b) i   c) ii   d) i   e) i

Lynda's story
f) ii   g) ii   h) ii

VOCABULARY

Entertainment

a) orchestra   b) instruments   c) stage   d) stalls
e) cast   f) tabloid

Intensifying adjectives

a) 4   b) 7   c) 6   d) 3   e) 8   f) 5   g) 2   h) 1

Adjectives and prepositions

a) at   b) of   c) with   d) of   e) for   f) in
g) on   h) in

GRAMMAR

Present, Present Perfect or Past?

a) 1 has just announced
   2 was speaking
   3 is still going on

b) 1 have found
   2 disappeared
   3 have been questioning / are questioning
   4 has been charged

c) 1 is finally beginning / has finally begun
   2 were released
   3 been falling / fallen
   4 reached

Duration

b) i) How long have you been living / have you lived in
      your flat?
   ii) I've been living / I've lived there since 1984.

c) i) How long has he had the car?
   ii) He's had it for five years

d) i) How long has Anne been travelling?
   ii) She's been travelling for three months.

e) i) How long have you been feeling ill?
   ii) I've been feeling ill since last Monday.

Present Perfect Simple or Continuous?

b) I've written; I haven't finished
c) I've been eating
d) I've already eaten; drunk
e) She has been teaching; she has decided

PRONUNCIATION

Silent letters

b) handsome
c) honest
d) thumb
e) knife
f) sandwich
g) receipt
h) bomb
i) autumn
j) doubt
k) knee
l) whisky

WRITING

Dictation

a) I have to make the decision on Wednesday.
b) He's got a lot of experience in business.
c) You must definitely take the medicine.
d) Unfortunately the weather is awful.
e) Is it necessary to give you my diary?
f) Which patient is waiting?
g) I don't believe that they're foreigners.
h) It's especially difficult if they want separate rooms.

Unit 4

LISTENING

Before listening

1

chess; roulette; draughts

2

a) winnings   b) jackpot   c) stake   d) dealer   e) token

Listening

1

a) Nevada   b) over 6 billion dollars
c) fruit machines; video poker   d) more than 700,000
e) casinos; motels; souvenir shops; porn cinemas;
   pawnbrokers   f) a parking lot

2

a) fantasy land   b) 365   c) 100,000
d) keeps winning   e) 600   f) 2 million
g) a mink coat, a champagne breakfast and a hairdo
h) older people

GRAMMAR

Sequence of tenses

b) While Louise was cooking / cooked the lunch the
   children were sleeping / slept.
c) After I had done the shopping I went home.
d) When I saw the burglary I (immediately) rang the police.
e) As soon as I had checked into the hotel I phoned my
   boss.
f) When Sarah was doing the ironing she heard a loud
   noise outside.
g) When Sarah heard a loud noise she went outside to
   investigate.

Past Perfect Simple or Continuous?

b) had driven
c) had forgotten
d) had been shopping
e) had been skiing; had broken
f) had been writing; had written

Narrative forms

a) 2 hurt
   3 saw
   4 didn't realise
   5 had broken

b) 1 went
   2 had phoned / phoned
   3 was happening / had happened
   4 discovered
   5 had escaped
   6 had killed
   7 was trying / tried
   8 were lying

c) 1 heard
   2 looked
   3 had been playing
   4 (had been) watching
   5 began / were beginning
   6 had told / had been telling

VOCABULARY

Phrasal verbs

b) take after   c) take up   d) take in   e) take off
f) take in   g) take off

Common errors

a) I've *left* my book in my room.
b) I'm just going to go and *bring* it here.
c) She *missed* the train because she was late.
d) Some of my class are going on a *trip* next month.
e) Remember to *check* your work before handing it in.
f) Marcela is *waiting for* Nikos outside the gate
g) Next week I am going to *take* the exam.

Verbs and prepositions

b) for   c) with   d) to   e) in   f) about   g) on
h) at   i) on   j) at

Places

b) 7   c) 5   d) 4   e) 6   f) 1   g) 2   h) 8

WRITING

Linking expressions

1

b) However   c) While   d) so   e) Since   f) to

2
Examples:
a) a cat
b) she can't speak much French
c) they had to sell it
d) I went to buy a cold drink
e) I can't really afford it
f) the pipes are frozen
g) learn English
h) I had some prawns

Unit 5

READING

1
Examples:
a) The two people have to trust each other.
b) You can pursue your outside interests.
c) You have to be careful not to do the same number of hours as full-time colleagues.

2
a) True   b) False   c) False   d) True   e) True

3
a) What's Jane like?
b) Who is writing a book?
c) Are they well-qualified?
d) Would Jane like her husband to job-share?

GRAMMAR

Mixed question forms

b) Who did you go to the cinema with?
c) Where did you buy your jacket?
d) Who will / Who's going to give me a lift?
e) Did you have a good time?
f) How much / What does it weigh?
g) Who ate the biggest pizza?
h) When are you going to clean your shoes?
i) What's Brian like?
j) What does he look like?

Less direct and reported questions

b) . . . where the nearest post office is?
c) . . . if / whether they found any oil in the desert?
d) . . . how many symphonies Mozart wrote?
e) . . . if / whether I had been (was) happy at school.
f) . . . how often Mike went swimming.

Question tags

1
a) 5   b) 1   c) 6   d) 2   e) 3   f) 4
2
b) hasn't he? / has he?   e) won't he? / will he?
c) did it?   f) have you?
d) will you?   g) could I?

Word order

b) I refuse to answer that question.
c) Please explain the rules to us.
d) I'm flying home to Mali on Friday.
   (On Friday I'm . . .)
e) Everyone enjoyed themselves at the party very much.
   (Everyone very much enjoyed . . .)
f) Have you reported the accident to the police?
g) I'll pay you for the tickets at 8 o'clock tomorrow.
   (. . . tomorrow at 8 o'clock)

VOCABULARY

Men and women

a) M   b) F   c) B   d) M   e) M   f) F   g) F   h) M
i) M   j) F   k) F   l) F   m) F   n) B

Synonyms and antonyms

b) S: obstinate   A: flexible
c) S: nude   A: clothed
d) S: mean   A: generous
e) S: excitable   A: calm
f) S: brave   A: cowardly
g) S: prosperous   A: hard up

PRONUNCIATION

Question tags

The speaker is sure about questions: a), d), f)

WRITING

1

a) 2   b) 1   d) 3

2

a) pcm　　　　d) mod. cons　　g) CH
b) ono　　　　e) hrs　　　　　h) eves
c) VGC　　　　f) pw　　　　　i) bed

3

Example:
LONDON hse. 10 mins Oxf Circus. Lge dbl rm. to let. Suit yng cpl. No smkrs. CH. £80pw 081-636 1555. wknds

Unit 6

LISTENING

1

b) 6   c) 5   d) 2   e) 8   f) 1   g) 9   h) 7   i) 10   j) 3

3

1 lower
2 back
3 muscles
4 legs
5 working on word processor
6 standing up for a period of time (e.g. rugby match)
7 a few days
8 riding accident
9 painkillers
10 back exercises
11 X-ray
12 damage
13 pain relief
14 physiotherapy
15 over-exert herself (do aerobics)

VOCABULARY

Collocation

1

b) throat, lips
c) muscle
d) knee, ankle, wrist
e) skull

2

a) on   b) under   c) from   d) in   e) from   f) of

Medical terms

b) diet   c) injection   d) outbreak   e) insomnia

GRAMMAR

Obligation

1

Examples:
b) She needn't have run.
c) I must go and get them in.
d) You should lock it.
e) I suppose they feel they don't need to get married.
f) In that case he'll have to go and buy one.

2

a) have to　　　　d) shouldn't
b) should　　　　e) needn't have worried
c) needn't　　　　f) don't have to

Advice

Examples:
a) ii) . . . cash a cheque at the bank.
b) i) . . . ban cars from city centres.
   ii) . . . you encourage(d) people to travel by train.
c) i) . . . have a holiday.
   ii) . . . working in the mornings only.
d) i) . . . I'd move.
   ii) . . . to spend some money on it.
e) i) . . . go there again.
   ii) . . . learnt to behave.

PRONUNCIATION

Connected speech

1

b) 7   c) 8   d) 8   e) 8

2

a) You needn't have brought any more wine.
b) I really mustn't miss the bus.
c) Why did you have to be so rude?
d) What do you think I ought to do?
e) I think she should have left home earlier.

Unit 7

READING

1

a) taxying
b) turning into the wind
c) reaching flying speed
d) reaching safety speed
e) climbing

2

Picture 2 indicates level speed.
a) down
b) up

3

a) . . . it stalls.
b) . . . reduce speed.
c) . . . raising the aircraft's nose.
d) . . . a plane is no longer moving at its flying speed.

GRAMMAR

Talking about the future

1

Not likely forms:
a) A: do
   B: am going to
b) A: Shall you bring / Are you bringing
   B: 'm letting
c) A: the film's ending
   B: do you do
d) A: go
   B: 'm seeing
e) A: are not forgetting
   B: 'll take you

2

Examples:
a) B: . . . I'll go by train.
b) B: . . . were going to . . .
c) B: . . . I'm going to make it
d) B: . . . 'll do it for you.
e) B: . . . I'm seeing my parents.

Future time expressions

Examples:
a) 're
b) go
c) 'll tell; can
d) is born
e) stops
f) win; 'll cut

VOCABULARY

American English

a) 3   b) 8   c) 7   d) 1   e) 5   f) 9   g) 2   h) 10   i) 6   j) 4

Prepositional phrases

b) on   c) by   d) at   e) by   f) at   g) on   h) in

Collocation

b) turn   c) make   d) do   e) change   f) take
g) give   h) have

Forming adjectives and adverbs

b) delightful
c) affectionately
d) unprecedented
e) unnecessarily
f) aggressive
g) poisonous
h) unshaven
i) thoughtless

WRITING

Written style

Example:
. . . were trying to get a drink. The stewards and stewardesses were in a terrible mood and it was chaos, when suddenly the plane went into a dive. Nobody knew what it could be since the weather was fine and there was no storm. Everyone was screaming. Even the cabin crew were on their backs or lying on top of the passengers. It was quite a sight. Bottles fell out of the lockers and people grabbed hold of each other. I was terrified but after what seemed like hours we pulled out of the dive and ten minutes later we landed. The reason for the incident was that the flight crew had fallen asleep because they had been on duty for 20 hours at a stretch. We thought this was completely wrong and complained at the airport. We even threatened to write to the Prime Minister. I'm never going by plane again. The next time we go on holiday we're going by boat.

Unit 8

LISTENING

Before listening

1
a) ii)   b) i)

2
a) Friendship 7   b) John Glenn   c) February 20th

Listening

d) near dawn
e) loose part
f) excited
g) overheating
h) return to earth
i) no
j) disappointed

GRAMMAR

Future Continuous or Perfect?

b) will have got back
c) 'll be waiting
d) 'll be thinking
e) will have finished
f) 'll be leaving

Future review

Examples:
b) we'll be lying
c) 'll carry it
d) are you going to retire
e) will have been cleared up
f) does it start
g) are you going (to go)
h) is going to collapse

Complex sentences

b) i) Although I can hear it clearly now, it still sounds awful.
   ii) Hearing it clearly now, it still sounds awful.
c) i) As soon as (When) I get paid tomorrow, I'll give you the money.
   ii) On getting paid tomorrow, I'll give you the money.
d) i) When I saw the film on TV, I thought it was old-fashioned.
   ii) Seeing the film (Having seen the film) on TV, I thought it was old-fashioned.
e) i) Since he's tall, he's always bumping his head.
   ii) Being tall, he's always bumping his head.

VOCABULARY

Words often confused

1
a) path   b) directions   c) way   d) direction

2
a) discovered   b) lonely   c) lack   d) reward
e) remind   f) same

Prepositions of time

1 from   2 to   3 at   4 before   5 until   6 by
7 in   8 between   9 for   10 on

Idiomatic expressions

b) the best of both worlds
c) dead to the world
d) thinks the world
e) worlds apart
f) a world of good

Compound adjectives

b) a green-eyed cat
c) a three-star hotel
d) a strong-minded teacher
e) a left-handed woman
f) a big-headed actor
g) a three-mile run
h) home-made bread

WRITING

Abbreviations

a) 4   b) 6   c) 2   d) 5   e) 7   f) 8   g) 1   h) 3

Dictation

1

This is likely to be an important week, with the challenge of change in the air, mixed with unusual opportunities and a number of fortunate coincidences. You should be keen to go; if you do not make a move you could lose your chance.

3

You'll be in a difficult mood, determined to be different just for the sake of it. Friends will find you entertaining but annoying; your social life will be lively but you'll almost certainly be offered advice you have no patience with.

Unit 9

READING

1

Examples:
b) She got snow-blindness because she didn't have any goggles.
c) Although someone had covered her with sheepskins as an act of kindness to keep her warm, they gave her flea-bites.

2

a) To protect her from the strong light of the sun reflected off the snow.
b) Because there was food as well as human and animal life, in comparison with the deserted areas she had just come from.
c) Because she was suffering from snow-blindness.

Vocabulary in context

1

a) i   b) ii   c) i   d) ii   e) i

2

b) lashings   c) tossed   d) panting   e) excruciating
f) wrenched

GRAMMAR

Review of the article

a) Last night, *a* man was *the* victim of *a* violent attack. *The* identity of *the* man is being kept secret.
b) Put *the* baby back to bed, turn off *the* light and go to sleep.
c) I think that friends, peace of mind and *a* good job are *the* most important things in life.
d) We always have lamb for lunch on Sundays. Would you like *an* egg on toast if I get it for you?
e) When I arrived in England, I bought a copy of *The Independent*, *a* typical British newspaper.
f) This morning I got in *a* taxi and went to *the* National Gallery in Trafalgar Square.
g) I think *the* English are very arrogant, particularly *the* rich.
h) So you left school at 16, went to university two years later and got *a* degree in economics.
i) Where did you say *the* university was?
j) This morning she did *the* shopping, went to *the* doctor and then went to work.

Could / (was/were) able to / managed to

a) finally managed to
b) were able to
c) could
d) wasn't able to

e) Could you
f) was able to
g) were able to

Used for

b) It's used for looking at distant objects.
c) It's used for drying hair.
d) It's used for watering plants / watering the garden.
e) It's used for putting in screws.

As/like

Correct sentences: a), d), e), h)

WRITING

Sounds and spelling

1

a) bel*ie*ve   *ea*ch   bl*ee*d   c*ei*ling   p*eo*ple
b) r*ou*gh   t*o*ffee   *ph*otograph   ha*lf*
c) ch*ai*r   th*e*re   pr*ay*er   r*a*re   p*ea*r (p*ai*r)
d) ba*dg*e   *j*oke   s*o*ldier   *u*rge

2

b) centre   c) cheque book   d) analyse
e) jewellery   f) catalogue   g) traveller   h) pyjamas

VOCABULARY

Phrasal verbs

1

b) A bomb went off outside our hotel.
c) Please don't tell me off.
d) How long will it take us to set up the company / set the company up?
e) I wish we could talk it over.

2

2 go away	7 called for
3 go back	8 set off for
4 go round	9 run away
5 pick him up	10 make for
6 see me off	

Animals

1

a) a flock of sheep
b) a herd of cows
c) a swarm of bees
d) a pack of wolves
e) a school of whales
f) a shoal of fish

2

b) cows   c) horses   d) dogs   e) monkeys
f) snakes   g) lions   h) parrots   i) mice

Unit 10

READING

1

a) 5   b) 3   c) 4   d) 2   e) 1

2

Invented story: 3

3

a) False   b) True   c) False   d) True   e) False   f) False
g) True   h) True

GRAMMAR

Present, Present Perfect or Past?

1 broadcast	9 had been living
2 had heard	10 has bought
3 has become	11 has made
4 used to live	12 attends
5 snowed	13 has just finished
6 had been worrying	14 appeared
7 decided	15 is writing
8 saw	

Question forms

b) How much does the Managing Director earn?
c) Which wild animals don't eat meat?
d) What is your steak like?
e) Can you tell me where the bank is?
f) Whose is that car?

Modals of obligation

b) You must phone
c) You needn't have left / You didn't need to leave / You didn't have to leave
d) You mustn't use
e) You should buy
f) You needn't buy / You don't need to buy / You don't have to buy
g) I had to eat

Future forms

a) A: are going to
   B: I'll
b) A: will be doing
   B: I'll have finished; I'll be
c) A: will you be going
   B: I'm going
d) A: will you have finished
   B: I'll

VOCABULARY

Word building

1

a) freedom	d) lengthen
b) unhappiness	e) patience
c) discovery	f) thoughtless

Prepositions

a) on   b) with   c) on   d) from   e) on   f) for

Phrasal verbs

b) gone up	e) told off
c) see off	f) taken up
d) set up	

Definitions

a) travel agent	e) flock
b) stubborn	f) positive
c) cowardly	g) stage
d) pavement	

PRONUNCIATION

Dictation

Stressed words are given in italics.
a) Are you *driving* or going by *train*?
b) Do you take *sugar* in your *tea*?
c) She'd like some *lemonade* and a packet of *crisps*.
d) She can play *tennis* but she can't *swim* at all.
e) I must *go* or I'll be *late*.
f) Is he going to stay for *tea*?

WRITING

Review of linking expressions

1

a) while   b) so   c) However   d) Afterwards
e) although

2

a) When   b) As   c) because   d) but
e) Meanwhile   f) As a result

Unit 11

READING

1

b) On a camp-site at Ayers Rock (in the Australian outback).
c) On a spring night in 1980.
d) She was abducted by a dingo.
e) That Lindy Chamberlain killed her.
f) Because she seemed to the media to be unemotional and uncaring.
g) Three and a half years.
h) Meryl Streep and Sam Neill.

2

a) . . . they wanted to believe dingoes do not eat children (particularly in a holiday area).
b) . . . evil in things.
c) . . . what the newspapers and television tell them.
d) . . . how they present themselves.

VOCABULARY

Collocation

a) deeply   b) deadly   c) highly   d) strictly   e) loosely
f) considerably   g) bitterly

Phrasal verbs

1
b) 2   c) 1   d) 3   e) 4

2
b) gone up   e) went off
c) goes with   f) going on
d) go for   g) went for

Word association

b) horse   c) newspaper   d) flower   e) fruit   f) television
g) tennis   h) baby   i) dog   j) hospital

GRAMMAR

Mixed conditional forms

1
b) iii   c) ii   d) ii   e) i

2
b) If you save half the money yourself, I'll let you go on holiday.
c) If you want to go to Australia, you have to have a visa.
d) If I weren't working, I'd come.
e) Unless you change your clothes, you can't come with us.
f) If I could drive, I'd give you a lift to the station.

Wish and *if only*

b) 'If only *I could afford* a faster car.'
c) 'I wish *I could give up* smoking.'
d) 'I wish *it would stop* raining.'
e) 'If only *I could stop* biting my nails.'
f) 'I wish *it were* easier.'
g) 'I wish *he would go* home.'

PRONUNCIATION

Dictation

1
b) 9   c) 8   d) 9   e) 8   f) 8

2
a) *If he's coming, I'm sure he'll give you a* lift.
b) *I think she'd agree if she were* asked.
c) *Can you phone me if you're* coming?
d) *I really wish I could see without my* glasses.
e) *We'll be there unless it's* raining.
f) *If I were him, I'd leave* tomorrow.

WRITING

Punctuation

92 South Street,
Preston PR2 4XB
2nd March 1992

Dear Julia,
Thanks for your letter, which I have been meaning to reply to for ages. I have been very busy recently, but now my exams have finished and so I can finally write back to you.

I was glad to hear that you're well and happy, and that you've settled down in your new house. It sounds fantastic!

One of the reasons I was writing, actually, is to ask you if Tim and I could come and stay sometime in the Easter holidays. We both have two weeks off, and so we thought we could drive down and see you all. Of course if this isn't convenient you must say so. You know me well enough for that, I hope!

Did I tell you that I've changed my job at last? I'm now working at a school in Lancaster, and I'm much happier there than at the other one. I'm still living here, though – it only takes 20 minutes to drive.

Anyway, that's all for now. We're rushing out, as usual. Lots of love to all the family and a big hug to you. Hope to see you soon.

Love,
Sheila

Unit 12

VOCABULARY

Crime and punishment

1
a) burglary   b) bigamy   c) blackmail   d) smuggling
e) trespassing   f) mugging   g) rape   h) murder

Word square

2

Crime	Verb	Person
burglary	burgle	burglar
bigamy	commit bigamy	bigamist
blackmail	blackmail	blackmailer
smuggling	smuggle	smuggler
trespassing	trespass	trespasser
mugging	mug	mugger
rape	rape	rapist
murder	murder	murderer

3

a) 6 b) 4 c) 3 d) 8 e) 5 f) 1 g) 7 h) 2

Nouns and prepositions

a) of b) with c) in d) with e) on
f) of/in g) in h) between i) for

LISTENING

1

a) False b) True c) False d) True e) True f) True
g) False

3

a) They had an argument over a parking place.
b) He took one from a restaurant.

Vocabulary in context

a) U b) P c) P d) U e) U

GRAMMAR

Past conditional and *wish*

b) i) He wishes he hadn't been rude to his boss.
   ii) If he hadn't been rude to his boss, he wouldn't have
       lost his job.
c) i) They wish they hadn't invested in gold / the price
       hadn't dropped.
   ii) If they hadn't invested in gold / the price hadn't
       dropped, the company wouldn't have gone out of
       business.
d) i) We wish we'd gone on holiday in July.
   ii) If we'd gone on holiday in July, we would have been
       able to swim.
e) i) We wish we'd brought our camera.
   ii) If we'd brought our camera, we would have got a
       picture of the sunset.
f) i) I wish I hadn't forgotten / had remembered to put a
       stamp on his card.
   ii) If I hadn't forgotten to put a stamp on his card, he
       would have got it in time for his birthday.
g) i) I wish you had told me your boss was coming to
       dinner.
   ii) If you had told me your boss was coming to dinner, I
       would have gone shopping.
h) i) I wish the sea hadn't been rough.
   ii) If the sea hadn't been rough, I would have enjoyed
       the journey.

Wish and *if only*

b) had
c) would decide
d) weren't going out/
   hadn't gone out
e) hadn't written
f) would stop
g) lived

Criticisms

b) should have left earlier
c) should have told someone
d) should have asked her first
e) shouldn't have been driving so fast
f) should have taken more care
g) should have been wearing / worn your seatbelt

WRITING

Summary writing

2

Example summary (59 words):

Pamela Megginson battered her 79-year-old millionaire
lover, Alec Hubbers, to death because he had just told her
he was leaving her for another woman.

Megginson had shared his lavish lifestyle for thirteen
years, until the arrival of this new woman.

Contrary to expectation Megginson was found guilty of
murder at her trial, and sentenced to life imprisonment.

Unit 13

READING

1

a) France b) Israel c) Zimbabwe

3

b) Britain c) Ireland d) France

4

Examples:
a) Because there are too few houses for people to live in.
b) They have to get someone to help them find a way of
   coming together.
c) Because all you have to do is change your civil status by
   an ordinary legal process.
d) They have to have a cooling-off period imposed by
   temple officials.

GRAMMAR

The passive

1

a) i b) i c) ii

2

a) was sent
b) can be built
c) has just been jailed; to be taken
d) are put

3

b) From next week all managers will be given a 70 per cent
   pay rise.
c) They must be taken with water.
d) How many times has it been performed before?
e) It is being decorated at this moment.

Pronouns

b) itself c) me d) herself e) himself f) yours; it

Have (get) something done

c) We usually have (get) our groceries delivered for us.
d) Diane had (got) her hair dyed red last week.
e) Did the teacher correct your homework?
f) Have you had your room cleaned yet?
g) At last the plumber has installed their shower.

VOCABULARY

Idiomatic expressions

b) hair   c) head   d) foot   e) hand   f) eyes
g) back   h) nose   i) leg   j) tongue

Newspaper headlines

b) backs   c) bid   d) slams   e) hits   f) talks
g) axed.   h) shelved

WRITING

Letter of invitation

Example:

> 13 Holland Street,
> Merrow.
> 2nd May 1992

Dear Jean,

We would like to invite you to our daughter Elizabeth's wedding to Richard Mason on Saturday 12th July.

There will be a short ceremony at the Registry Office in Woking at 3 o'clock. After that there will be a reception at the Lamb Inn, which is also in Woking. We would be very happy if you were able to make both of these.

We hope you will be able to come but do you think you could let us know either way. Many thanks and look forward to seeing you.

> Yours sincerely,
> David and Marion Walters

Unit 14

LISTENING

1
Situations a), c), d)

2
b) . . . shop (and) the shop assistants are talking to each other when you are standing there.
c) . . . train (and) other people are trying to push on.
d) . . . car (and) someone takes your parking spot.
e) . . . out of chip papers (in the town).
f) . . . 'Yes, please' and 'No, thank you'.

3
a) When they try to push in in bus queues
b) They change character and become very aggressive.

GRAMMAR

Verb + object (+ *to*) + base form

b) She invited me to go to the cinema.
c) I want you to find someone else.
d) It makes me feel unhappy.
e) Remind me not to leave it on tonight.
f) He would like you to go with him.
g) He ordered me to take a month's rest.

-ing or *to?*

1
b) . . . having stolen / stealing the money.
c) . . . to see Paul this evening.
d) . . . not to travel economy class on that airline!
e) . . . paying bills until I have to.
f) . . . putting the money in my wallet.

2
a) mending   e) to stop playing
b) stealing   f) to make
c) to play   g) hearing; to say
d) skiing   h) driving

Expressing preferences

b) rather   c) prefer   d) would rather   e) would rather
f) would prefer   g) prefer

VOCABULARY

Connotation

b) N   c) P   d) N   e) P   f) N   g) P   h) P
i) N   j) N   k) P   l) N   m) P

Ambiguity

b) i and ii   c) ii and iii   d) i and ii   e) i and iii   f) i and ii

Proverbs

b) policy   c) cat   d) eggs   e) quarrel   f) waters
g) iron   h) Actions   i) rains

WRITING

Spelling

a) hear   b) passed   c) It's; there   d) quite
e) Whose   f) read   g) friend   h) whether
i) choice

Unit 15

READING

1
a) the wife of the men's boss.
b) she is very strict with the men.

2
Have to: rise at dawn, perform household chores, work as valets to the highest-ranking wrestlers, endure fearsome workouts, do all the cooking.
Not allowed to: go out at night, leave their slippers out of line.

3
b) lines 19–21   c) lines 27-31   d) lines 33-35

4
a) They have left. / They have died.
b) She doesn't feel pity for them in the ring but feels pity for them at the stable because of their very disciplined life.
c) The life the young apprentice wrestlers find in the stable will be a shock to them.
d) It builds up the wrestler's fat.
e) They only eat twice a day; they are not used to the work; some don't like the food.

VOCABULARY

Numbers

1
a) 4, 345³/4
b) 5 × 7 = 35
c) 301. 79
d) 68%
e) 21 ÷ 3 = 7
f) 633 0950
g) £10.49
h) 15–0
i) 4–0
j) 2–2

2
a) Two hundred and forty thousand
b) Fourteen and a third
c) Eighteen minus seven plus four is/equals fifteen
d) Eleven pounds sixty one (pence)
e) Nineteen ninety three

Idioms

b) rings a bell
c) break the ice
d) meet *you* halfway
e) close shave
f) on the cards
g) in the dark

GRAMMAR

Quantity

1
b) loaf   c) bunch   d) tube   e) packet
f) tin   g) pile   h) jar

2
a) job
b) advice
c) chair
d) luggage
e) pound coins
f) information

Compounds of *some, any, no, every*

a) anything   b) everywhere   c) no one
d) somewhere   e) anyone   f) everything

Each, another, both, either, etc.

b) either
c) Neither; nor; has
d) None; are
e) All; are
f) the other
g) Each; has
h) another

PRONUNCIATION

Words with the same spelling

1
b) minute   c) wind   d) conduct   e) live
f) present

2
b) /ˈmɪnɪt/   c) /wɪnd/   d) /ˈkɒndʌkt/
e) /laɪv/   f) /prɪˈzent/

3
a) conduct   b) present   c) record   d) wind
e) live   f) minute

WRITING

Punctuation

a) Professor Jones was last seen in Hyde Park in November.
b) Where's your newspaper's principles?
c) Add the fish, oysters and herbs, followed by the tomato.
d) 'It was lucky I discovered her,' said Mr Biggs.
e) Dr Jones, lecturer in philosophy at King's College, said: 'I'm looking forward to the day when this college listens to students' views.'

Unit 16

LISTENING

1
b) Dick: 3
c) Chris: 1

2
Examples:
b) very colourful
c) the atmosphere

3
Examples:
a) When your team gets a free kick and gets the chance to score a goal.
b) Getting a goal.
c) The smell of beer and hot dogs.
d) When nobody hits the ball.
e) When it is hit a long way, high in the air.
f) Because he likes to cheer them on.

VOCABULARY

Word building

Adjective	Adverb	Noun	Verb
exciting	excitingly	excitement	excite
argumentative	argumentatively	argument	argue
educational	educationally	education	educate
legal	legally	legality	legalise
reasonable	reasonably	reason	reason
embarrassing	embarrassingly	embarrassment	embarrass
thoughtful	thoughtfully	thought	think
fantastic	fantastically	fantasy	fantasise
decisive	decisively	decision	decide
accused	accusingly	accusation	accuse

Similes

1
a) 6 b) 3 c) 5 d) 9 e) 8 f) 4 g) 2 h) 1 i) 7

2
b) . . . as old as the hills.
c) . . . as cool as a cucumber.
d) . . . as clean as a whistle.
e) . . . as sharp as a knife.
f) . . . as white as a sheet.
g) . . . as keen as mustard.
h) . . . as good as gold.
i) . . . as light as a feather.

Foreign words and phrases

b) pro rata
c) incognito
d) siesta
e) macho
f) status quo
g) ad nauseam
h) Bon voyage
i) vice versa
j) cul-de-sac
k) faux pas

GRAMMAR

Modals

b) must c) may d) should e) can't
f) May / Can g) can't h) mustn't

Reference words

2 Deirdre's mother
3 Deirdre
4 Deirdre's mother
5 sports/open days / school concerts
6 The memory
7 Deirdre
8 James
9 Deirdre and James
10 James

WRITING

Dialogue of complaint

Example:
A: Good afternoon. Reception.
B: Can you help me? My television isn't working. Could someone have a look at it?
A: I'm sorry. I'm afraid I can't get it looked at today because the electrician is away.
B: There must be someone who could sort it out. Can't you come up?
A: No, sorry. We are very busy and I can't leave reception.
B: That's ridiculous. If you can't do anything then I want to speak to the manager.
A: I'm sorry but the manager isn't available today.
B: I'll see her tomorrow then. Meanwhile I insist on moving to another room where the television works.
A: Certainly. I'll arrange that for you immediately.
B: Thanks. That's better than nothing.

Unit 17

LISTENING

1
Arguments: a), c), e)

2
Arguments: b), d), e)

3
a) When she was nine.
b) The lead hound ripped the fox to pieces.
c) All new members have to have it done – it's tradition.
d) She is against it.

Vocabulary in context

a) very unpleasant; illegal
b) plants grown by farmers; animals kept on a farm
c) big help
d) animals that kill or eat other animals
e) kindest

GRAMMAR

Reported speech

a) . . . why she hunted.
b) . . . hunting was a marvellous way of relaxing, and she loved the countryside. . . . she had gone / went on her first hunt when she was six, but had taken it up / took it up seriously when she was sixteen. . . . was part of the rule of nature.
c) . . . if hunting was a cruel way to kill foxes.
d) . . . it was the only . . . the fox either got away or died in seconds.

Direct speech

'This week we have been working in groups of about fifteen people. Our aim is to make sure that the fox stays alive and doesn't get caught,' she replied.
'What exactly do you do?' I wanted to know.
'We blow horns to confuse the hounds, and sit on gates so the hunt can't pass,' she explained.

Reporting verbs

1
a) . . . Max to take his keys.
b) . . . me to wait until the next day / tomorrow.
c) . . . us to come/go to dinner next / the following Friday.
d) . . . her not to go out in the car.
e) . . . me to get out of his office that minute.
f) . . . us to come / go to the party.

2
a) . . . congratulated David on winning first prize.
b) . . . accused Tim of scratching her car the day before / yesterday.
c) . . . suggested going / we went in his car.
d) . . . apologised for being late.
e) . . . offered to get us a drink.
f) . . . complained that the test wasn't / hadn't been fair.

VOCABULARY

Adjectives and nouns

b) bed, ticket
c) food, weather, drink
d) weather, wine
e) pullover, book
f) drink, cheese

Synonyms and antonyms

1

b) amusing   c) hard   d) spicy   e) simple
f) courageous   g) chatty   h) great / fantastic   i) wealthy
j) messy

2

b) mild   c) single   d) return   e) soft   f) soft / quiet
g) sweet   h) dry   i) shallow   j) deep / heavy

Phrasal verbs

a) put up with
b) Get on with
c) get through to
d) get away with it
e) get out of
f) run out of

Unit 18

READING

1

a) False   b) True   c) False   d) True   e) True   f) False

2

a) Grown men and women, even very strong ones.
b) About 200.
c) Special blankets, pillows and toys.
d) Sprinkle them in their back gardens, or where they used to take their dogs for walks.
e) Plant shrubs, leave flowers or just think about their pets.
f) A burial service, or organ music.

GRAMMAR

Defining relative clauses

1

a) who / that   b) which / that   c) whose
d) where / in which   e) why

2

a) Ben Johnson
b) salt
c) Dustin Hoffman
d) Bermuda Triangle
e) there isn't enough sun

Defining and non-defining relative clauses

b) The shop where I buy all my clothes is having a sale.
c) Pauline was telling me about her eldest daughter, who lives in Australia.
d) I need the newspaper that / which I threw away last night.
e) Kate, whose son is married to my cousin, is coming to stay at Christmas.

Participle clauses

b) waving   c) injured   d) chosen   e) wanting   f) sent
g) moving

Adjectives ending in -ing and -ed

a) disappointed   b) confused   c) embarrassed
d) amusing; bored   e) annoyed   f) satisfied
g) worrying

VOCABULARY

Word building

a) ambitious   b) resignation   c) patient
d) lengthen   e) explanation   f) modernise
g) crowded   h) heat   i) failure

Prepositional phrases

a) on   b) by   c) for   d) under   e) on   f) by   g) on
g) on   h) for   i) under   j) in

Confusing words

a) wedding   b) relatives   c) wear   d) reaches
e) beat   f) reward   g) bring   h) opportunity
i) fit   j) do

PRONUNCIATION

Vowel sounds

/iː/	/ʊ/	/e/
people	could	bury
piece	book	health
wheel	stood	any

/ʌ/	/ɒ/	/æ/
uncle	cough	match
young	watch	tap
does	bottle	can

/uː/	/ɑː/	/ɔː/
pool	half	lawn
move	aunt	bought
juice	can't	horse

/ɪ/	/ɜː/
build	fur
fill	earth
if	word

WRITING

Joining sentences

1

a) Whenever   b) until   c) in case   d) Both
e) unless   f) By the time   g) during

2

b) Because she had left her purse at home I lent her £5. /
She had left her purse at home, so I lent her £5.

c) I didn't have any breakfast, so I was starving all morning.
/ Because I didn't have any breakfast I was starving all
morning.

d) Adrian is very tall, whereas his sister is tiny. / Whereas
Adrian is very tall, his sister is tiny.

e) After they (had) bought a new house, they decided to
go abroad.

f) While I was looking everywhere for the letter the phone
was ringing non-stop. / The phone was ringing non-stop
while I was looking everywhere for the letter.

g) Unless you stay in bed and keep warm you won't get
better. / You won't get better unless you stay in bed and
keep warm.

h) Even though I really hate the idea of seafood, I'm going
to try it. / I'm going to try it, even though I really hate
the idea of seafood.

Unit 19

READING 1

1

a) A young woman and a middle-aged man.

b) In the park, while the man was feeding the ducks.

2

a) In the park at lunchtimes.

b) For several days.

c) In her twenties.

d) In his forties.

e) She is trying to find someone.

f) A civil servant.

3

a) He obviously doesn't want anyone to know that he has
connections with Elmston.

b) Someone who has a job with regular hours.

c) The conversation was becoming personal. He doesn't
want her to know anything about his personal life.

d) Open answer.

Vocabulary in context

a) crust   b) flirtation   c) gestured   d) trace
e) intriguing   f) prying

LISTENING 1

1

a)

2 . . . he had a lot of work to do at home.

3 . . . in his bedroom.

4 . . . six-year-old . . .

5 . . . knew the road well . . .

6 . . . slowly . . .

7 . . . was not on a pedestrian crossing.

8 . . . he had just been given a new job . . .

9 . . . he had just got married.

10 Nobody heard his brakes.

11 . . . was a policewoman, . . .

b)

2 . . . he couldn't concentrate at the office.

3 . . . in the shed.

4 . . . ten-year-old . . .

5 . . . didn't know the road (it was a diversion)

6 . . . exceeding the speed limit . . .

7 The girl was on a pedestrian crossing.

8 . . . he had been short-listed for a new job.

9 . . . he was getting married in a few days.

10 Several people heard the screech of brakes.

11 . . . was a former schoolfriend, or a relative, . . .

2

b) i   c) i   d) ii   e) i   f) i   g) ii   h) i

READING 2

1

a) the car number; photograph

b) a friend; used to have an MG

c) address and phone number; could contact her; his
friend's address

d) a photographer's; large buff-coloured envelope

e) Evening Gazette; a wedding report

f) he met a colleague (who started talking to him)

2

Examples:

a) . . . be looking for an excuse to get the girl's address
and phone number.

b) . . . the photograph of the car.

c) . . . have been trying to find the owners of the car.

d) . . . have thought he was watching the girl.

3

Examples:

a) held tightly

b) go

c) look through the pages / turn the pages

d) little bits / extracts

e) noise

f) very well indeed

LISTENING 2

1

a) It reminded Robert of his wedding photos in his album.

b) They were in the MG.

c) This is Robert now.

d) This was hiding two digits of the rear number plate (so it
was the same photo that the girl had talked about).

e) This was how the girl could find Robert's address.

f) This was where Robert told his wife he was going when
he went out.

g) The girl was getting Robert this when he killed her.

2

a) She must have gone to every local photographer to find
the negatives of the wedding photos.

b) She must have got a print of the negative.

c) She must have searched / been searching the
newspapers for a copy of the photo and his parents'
name and address.

3

Because Margaret's parents had emigrated and his parents
had died.

4

He was in the area and he had some information about his friend.

5

Open answer.

READING 3

a) Margaret's daughter / the girl that Robert had killed.
b) She had had a child before she met Robert, and had had her adopted.
c) Open answer.

Unit 20

GRAMMAR

Review of verb forms

2 can't say / wouldn't say
3 are studied
4 was being considered / was considered
5 drive
6 was spotted
7 hadn't faced
8 died
9 could suffer / could have suffered / had suffered
10 have been working / have worked
11 giving / to give
12 had
13 objected
14 was always travelling / always travelled
15 was / got involved
16 would marry / should marry / might marry / could marry
17 would have been / would be
18 Adapting
19 have now left
20 'll go

Conditionals; *wish*

b) she weren't / wasn't
c) had practised, he'd have / he might have
d) it would
e) had stayed / had booked in
f) won't come and see you (this evening); cook / buy
g) were; I'd see

Modals

a) can't
b) should have kept
c) don't have to
d) could have; needn't have
e) Did she have to go
f) must
g) can't
h) could

Spot the errors

b) If he doesn't hurry, . . .
c) The money was spent . . .
d) . . . of hers.
e) He ordered me to leave.
f) Please remember to lock the door . . .
g) . . . needs painting / to be painted.

Which is correct?

a) very good advice
b) anything
c) of them
d) , which pleased me
e) whose
f) leaving
g) told him
h) I was going

VOCABULARY

Colloquial language

a) Actions   b) away   c) off   d) up   e) hand
f) Fancy   g) gold   h) bell   i) nose   ·j) dark

Test your vocabulary

a) strictly   b) on   c) burglary   d) postpone
e) blond(e)-haired   f) plus; minus   g) to reason
h) a *faux pas*   i) beats

WRITING

Linking expressions

1 so   2 however   3 There   4 but   5 of course
6 on the whole   7 Yet   8 until   9 Since

Spelling

a) mistake   b) learning   c) social   d) Britain   e) different
f) When   g) people   h) meetings   i) stood   j) too

Punctuation

The Arabs stand closest to each other – less than an elbow away. The Swedes stand farthest apart – about an arm and a half. In Eastern Europe people like each other at a wrist's distance. The Latin folk don't mind at all if you move a lot closer – just outside the length of your or their elbow, whichever is the shorter. The British, someone said to me last week, are best described as 'fingertip people' and so are their American brothers and sisters.

1 Read the article and make notes to answer the following questions.

a) Who disappeared?

Azaria Chamberlain, a nine-week-old baby.

b) Where did she disappear?

_____

c) When?

_____

d) What did the parents think happened?

_____

e) What did the media think happened?

_____

f) Why were the public so sure the mother was guilty?

_____

g) How long was Lindy Chamberlain in jail?

_____

h) Who starred in the film version of the story?

_____

2 Complete these sentences, based on what the producer of the film said about the case.

a) People at Ayers Rock preferred not to believe that a dingo had killed the baby, because

_____

_____

b) Ordinary people like to find

_____

_____

c) The public forms its opinions based on

_____

_____

d) People judge others very quickly, depending on _____

_____

VOCABULARY

Collocation

Complete the sentences below with the most appropriate adverbs from the box.

highly deeply loosely bitterly deadly considerably strictly

a) The Chamberlains were _____ religious.

b) I'm afraid I found the book _____ boring. I can't understand why you liked it.

c) Come on! It's _____ unlikely to snow in July!

d) Smoking in classrooms is _____ forbidden.

e) The film and the book were only _____ connected.

f) Let's buy the paperback instead. It's _____ cheaper than the hardback version.

g) Louise cried all night. She's _____ disappointed about missing the school trip.

Phrasal verbs

1 Look at the different meanings of the phrasal verb *go through*. Write down the number of the definition which corresponds to the words in *italics* in the sentences below.

go through *phr v* **1** [T] (**go through** sthg.) to suffer or experience; ENDURE   **2** [T] (**go through** sthg.) to finish   **3** [I; T] (= **go through** sthg.) (of a law, etc.) to pass through or be accepted (by)   **4** [T] (**go through**. sthg) to practise (a ceremony or performance)   **5** [T] (**go through** sthg.) to look at or examine carefully

a) I'll just *check* my essay again to see if there are any mistakes. ___5___

b) I've managed to *spend* £100 this week just on food. _____

c) That family *has suffered* a lot this year. _____

d) Do you know if that new law *was agreed*? _____

e) Let's *do* Scene 2 *again*, shall we? _____

2 Replace the words or expressions in brackets with a phrasal verb from the box formed with *go*. Change the verb to an appropriate form. Some verbs are used more than once. Use your dictionary to help you.

go off   go with   go up   go for   go on

a) The milk has (*turned sour*) __gone off__. It smells disgusting.

b) The cost of housing has (*increased*) _____ alarmingly in the last ten years.

c) That dress (*matches*) _____ your eyes.

d) I think I'll (*choose*) _____ the salmon.

e) The alarm clock (*rang*) _____ at seven.

f) What is (*happening*) _____? There are police outside.

g) My dog (*attacked*) _____ the postman this morning.

Word association

Write down the word with which the four words in each group are associated. The first letter is given.

a) gears   steering wheel   clutch   boot
c*ar*_____

b) hoof   mane   neigh   saddle
h_____

c) tabloid   circulation   daily   editor
n_____

d) petal   leaf   bunch   stalk
f_____

e) pip   segment   peel   juice
f_____

f) aerial   channel   screen   programme
t_____

g) racket   umpire   net   match
t_____

h) nappy   bottle   toy   feed
b_____

i) paws   bark   lead   collar
d_____

j) surgeon   ward   operate   thermometer
h_____

GRAMMAR

Mixed conditional forms

1 Tick the phrases which best complete the sentences.

a) If you spent more time on your work:
  i) you won't make so many mistakes. ___
  ii) you don't make so many mistakes. ___
  iii) you wouldn't make so many mistakes. ✓

b) You can go when:
  i) you will finish. ___
  ii) you had finished. ___
  iii) you have finished. ✗

c) When I retire:
  i) I'd spend more time gardening. ___
  ii) I'll spend more time gardening. ✗
  iii) I spend more time gardening. ___

d) I don't like wine if:
  i) it will be too sweet. ___
  ii) it is too sweet. ✗
  iii) it were too sweet. ___

e) I might get a taxi if:
  i) it is raining. ✗
  ii) it will rain. ___
  iii) it would rain. ___

2 Write the second sentence based on the first. You may have to change the verb.

a) I can't buy it. I haven't got enough money.
If I *had enough money, I'd buy it.*

b) I'll let you go on holiday but you must save half the money yourself.
If you _____

c) You have to have a visa to go to Australia.
If you _____

d) Unfortunately, I'm working so I can't come.
If I _____

e) You can come with us, but not if you're going to wear those clothes!
Unless you _____

f) It's a pity I can't drive. Otherwise I could give you a lift to the station.
If I _____

Wish and *if only*

Molly is feeling a bit depressed and is talking about her life. Use *wish / if only* and the past or *wish / if only* and *would* to complete her exact words. Sometimes there is more than one possibility.

a) Her house is very small.
   'I wish _____ *I had* _____ a bigger one.'

b) She can't afford a faster car.
   'If only _____ a faster car.'

c) She can't give up smoking.
   'I wish _____ smoking.'

d) It has rained non-stop for five days and she wants it to stop.
   'I wish _____ raining.'

e) She bites her nails.
   'If only _____ biting my nails.'

f) French is such a difficult language.
   'I wish _____ easier.'

g) Unfortunately, her father is staying with her.
   'I wish _____ home.'

PRONUNCIATION

Dictation

1 [📼 11.1]   Listen to the recording and write down the number of words in each sentence. A contracted form counts as two words.

a) _____
   _____ lift. _13_

b) _____
   _____ asked. _____

c) _____
   _____ coming? _____

d) _____
   _____ glasses. _____

e) _____
   _____ raining. _____

f) _____
   _____ tomorrow. _____

2   Listen again and write down the missing words.

WRITING

Punctuation

Rewrite this letter on a separate sheet of paper, punctuating it and laying it out correctly. Divide the main part of the letter into five paragraphs.

92 south street
preston PR2 4XB
2nd march 1992

dear julia thanks for your letter which i have been meaning to reply to for ages i have been very busy recently but now my exams have finished and so i can finally write back to you i was glad to hear that youre well and happy and that youve settled down in your new house it sounds fantastic one of the reasons i was writing actually is to ask you if tim and i could come and stay sometime in the easter holidays we both have two weeks off and so we thought we could drive down and see you all of course if this isnt convenient you must say so you know me well enough for that i hope did i tell you that ive changed my job at last im now working at a school in lancaster and im much happier there than at the other one im still living here though it only takes 20 minutes to drive anyway thats all for now were rushing out as usual lots of love to all the family and a big hug to you hope to see you soon love sheila

• Crime and passion •

VOCABULARY

Crime and punishment

1   Look at the definitions of some crimes below and circle
words in the word square which make the name of the crimes.
You can read forwards or backwards, across, down or diagonally.

a) Breaking into a building and stealing
   something.
b) Being married to more than one person.
c) Getting money by threatening to tell a secret
   about somebody.
d) Taking things in and out of a country against
   the law.
e) Going on to privately owned land without
   permission.
f) Attacking and robbing someone.
g) Sexual assault.
h) The premeditated killing of someone.

```
T  R  E  S  P  A  S  S  I  N  G
F  L  T  M  H  D  P  Z  U  Q  O
O  Z  B  U  R  G  L  A  R  Y  L
M  C  L  G  P  H  J  C  Z  R  P
U  H  A  G  D  P  Q  M  A  E  X
V  Y  C  L  Z  J  Y  P  X  D  G
S  J  K  I  P  M  E  N  L  R  S
X  P  M  N  A  I  J  U  C  U  E
N  D  A  G  N  I  G  G  U  M  K
T  Q  I  O  Y  H  O  R  M  O  I
Y  B  L  S  L  E  A  D  F  R  T
```

2   Which verbs go with the nouns above? What is the person
called who commits these crimes? Complete the columns below.

Crime	Verb	Person
burglary	*burgle*	*burglar*
_____	_____	_____
_____	_____	_____
_____	_____	_____
_____	_____	_____
_____	_____	_____
_____	_____	_____

3 Number the following 1–8 in the order they happen.

a) the judge sums up _____

b) there is a trial _____

c) the accused is charged _____

d) the judge passes sentence _____

e) witnesses give their evidence _____

f) a crime is committed _1_

g) the jury reach a verdict _____

h) someone is arrested _____

Nouns and prepositions

Complete the sentences with suitable prepositions. In some cases there may be more than one possibility.

a) Have you had the results _____ your blood test yet?

b) If you're having difficulty _____ that exercise put your hand up.

c) There's been a dramatic rise _____ the crime rate.

d) If you have any problems _____ the car, phone me.

e) I'd appreciate your comments _____ my work.

f) I still can't see the advantage _____ going by car.

g) They've had lots of experience _____ that field.

h) There isn't a lot of difference _____ those two cheeses.

i) There's no hope _____ the country if it continues like this.

LISTENING

1 Before you listen, guess which of the following statements about murder are true. Do not write in the gaps yet.

a) Most murders are premeditated. _____

b) A lot of murders are caused by alcohol or drugs. _____

c) People who know each other do not often kill each other. _____

d) Murderers usually use more violence than is necessary to kill someone. _____

e) In the USA there are more than 10,000 murders each year. _____

f) In Britain there are no more than 1,000 murders a year. _____

g) It's quite difficult to get a gun anywhere in Britain. _____

2 [🔊 12.1] Listen to two extracts from a radio programme, in which doctors in Britain talk about their experience of homicide. Tick the statements above which are true.

3 Listen again and answer the following questions.

a) Why were three people stabbed?

_____

b) How did the man get a knife?

_____

Vocabulary in context

Divide these expressions from the recording into *P* (for *Premeditated*) and *U* (for *Unpremeditated*).

a) *sudden fit of passion* _____

b) *in cold blood* _____

c) *plan the deed* _____

d) *lose your temper* _____

e) *on the spur of the moment* _____

GRAMMAR

Past conditional and *wish*

Complete the sentences below, (i) to show regret, (ii) to show a desire for things to be different.

a) James went skiing. He broke his leg.
   i)   He wishes *he hadn't gone skiing.*
   ii) If he *hadn't gone skiing he wouldn't have broken his leg.*

b) Eric was rude to his boss. He lost his job.
   i)   He wishes _____
   ii) If he _____

c) The company invested in gold. The price of gold dropped and the company went out of business.
   i)   They wish _____
   ii) If they _____
        _____

d) We went on holiday in May but it was too cold to swim. Apparently it's much warmer in July.
   i)   We wish _____
   ii) If _____

e) We didn't bring our camera so we didn't get a picture of the sunset.
   i)   We wish _____
   ii) If we _____
        _____

f) I forgot to put a stamp on his card so he didn't get it in time for his birthday.
   i)   I wish _____
   ii) If I _____
        _____

g) You didn't tell me your boss was coming to dinner. I didn't go shopping today.
   i)   I wish you _____
   ii) If you _____
        _____

h) The sea was rough. I didn't enjoy the journey.
   i)   I wish _____
   ii) If the sea _____
        _____

Wish and *if only*

Complete the sentences using the cues in brackets in the Past or Past Perfect or with *would*.

a) These children are annoying me. I wish they (*go away*) *would go away.*

b) The police must often wish they (*have*) _____ more power to stop and search people.

c) I wish you (*decide*) _____ where you want to go on holiday. It'll be too late soon.

d) I wish we (*not go out*) _____ this evening.

e) Brian wishes he (*not write*) _____ his last novel. It was awful.

f) If only people (*stop*) _____ cutting down the rain forests.

g) Don't you ever wish you (*live*) _____ on a desert island, away from everybody?

Criticisms

Make criticisms of the situations below using *should(n't) have (been)* and the cues in brackets.

a) When I went out I left the milk on the table. When I got back it had gone off. (*put/fridge*) *I should have put it in the fridge.*

b) The concert started at 7.30, but he was late because of the rush-hour traffic. (*leave/earlier*) He _____

c) We went up a mountain last weekend. Nobody knew where we were. (*tell/someone*) You _____

d) We bought Granny a kitten for Christmas. Unfortunately, she didn't want it. (*ask her first*) We _____

e) I had a car accident. (*not drive so fast*) You _____

f) I did my homework very quickly and my teacher found lots of mistakes. (*take more care*) I _____

g) I stopped suddenly and hit my head against the windscreen. (*wear/seatbelt*) You _____

WRITING

Summary writing

1   Look at the article below and make notes on:
– what Pamela Megginson did.
– why she did it.
– what happened to her.
Include only the basic facts of what happened.

A woman scorned

Pamela Megginson, 61, of The Bishops Avenue, Hampstead, was convicted at the Old Bailey in September 1983 of murdering her millionaire lover and sentenced to life imprisonment.

Cold fear swept over Pamela Megginson as she sat in a candlelit restaurant on the French Riviera. Across the dinner table was the elderly lover she now hated so much she could no longer even bear to look at him. Self-made millionaire Alec Hubbers, aged 79, had just announced that he was leaving her for a younger woman. Less than an hour later he was dead. The jilted divorcee had battered him repeatedly over the head with a champagne bottle.

Megginson, the daughter of an English country squire, and Hubbers, a Russian-born Jewish immigrant, had fallen head over heels in love many years before. For 13 years she shared his London mansion and lavish lifestyle until suddenly and unexpectedly there was a new love in his life. The life of luxury was about to end and Megginson felt humiliated and rejected.

Many people who followed her trial were confident the jury would return a verdict of manslaughter, allowing the judge to deal leniently with the sad and defeated woman. But the jury of six men and six women found Megginson guilty of murder. The judge had no choice but to sentence her to life imprisonment. Her face crumpled and she wept as she was led away by two women prison officers.

---

2   On a separate sheet of paper, write a summary of the article in not more than 70 words. Organise it like this:

PARAGRAPH A: The murder

PARAGRAPH B: Background information

PARAGRAPH C: The trial

Just a piece of paper?

READING

1 Before reading about divorce in different parts of the world, guess in which country the following are possible. Underline your guesses.

a) You can get divorced quickly if both parties agree.

France/Ireland

b) Before marriage, men must save money for possible divorce.

Israel/Australia.

c) Men can have more than one wife.

Russia/Zimbabwe

2 Read the article and check your answers.

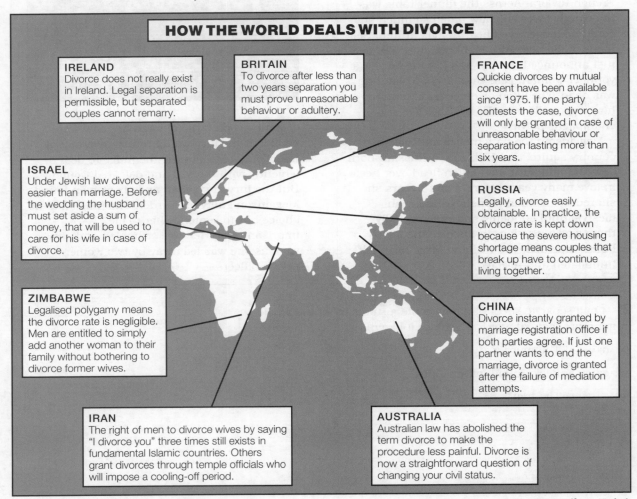

HOW THE WORLD DEALS WITH DIVORCE

IRELAND
Divorce does not really exist in Ireland. Legal separation is permissible, but separated couples cannot remarry.

BRITAIN
To divorce after less than two years separation you must prove unreasonable behaviour or adultery.

FRANCE
Quickie divorces by mutual consent have been available since 1975. If one party contests the case, divorce will only be granted in case of unreasonable behaviour or separation lasting more than six years.

ISRAEL
Under Jewish law divorce is easier than marriage. Before the wedding the husband must set aside a sum of money, that will be used to care for his wife in case of divorce.

RUSSIA
Legally, divorce easily obtainable. In practice, the divorce rate is kept down because the severe housing shortage means couples that break up have to continue living together.

ZIMBABWE
Legalised polygamy means the divorce rate is negligible. Men are entitled to simply add another woman to their family without bothering to divorce former wives.

CHINA
Divorce instantly granted by marriage registration office if both parties agree. If just one partner wants to end the marriage, divorce is granted after the failure of mediation attempts.

IRAN
The right of men to divorce wives by saying "I divorce you" three times still exists in fundamental Islamic countries. Others grant divorces through temple officials who will impose a cooling-off period.

AUSTRALIA
Australian law has abolished the term divorce to make the procedure less painful. Divorce is now a straightforward question of changing your civil status.

(from *Today*)

3   In which country:

a) can men divorce their wives by saying they want to? _Iran_____

b) is it hard to get divorced in less than two years? _____

c) is it possible for couples to separate legally but not get divorced? _____

d) must you normally wait six years if only one party wants the divorce? _____

4   Answer the following questions, according to the text. Use your dictionary to help you if necessary.

a) Why do couples in Russia often continue to live together after a divorce?

_____

b) What do Chinese couples have to do if only one partner wants to end the marriage?

_____

c) Why is divorce in Australia now easy?

_____

d) How do couples in Iran have to try to improve their relationship before getting a divorce?

_____

GRAMMAR

The passive

1   Tick the sentence in each pair which is the most natural.

a) i)

COATS MUST BE LEFT IN THE CLOAKROOM

_____

ii)

YOU MUST LEAVE YOUR COATS IN THE CLOAKROOM

_____

b) i) A: Who discovered penicillin?
   B: Fleming did.   _____

ii) A: Who discovered penicillin?
   B: It was discovered by Fleming.   _____

c) i) Oh, no! The phone company's disconnected our phone.   _____

ii) Oh, no! Our phone's been disconnected.   _____

2   Complete these news items using the verbs in brackets in the correct form.

a) A deadly tarantula (_send_) _____ to a wealthy divorcee yesterday.

b) Planners will decide tomorrow whether the office (_build_) _____.

c) Ian Marshal, who mugged a man twice in the same night, (_just, jail_) _____. Marshal asked for another offence (_take_) _____ into account.

d) Small shops may disappear unless the proposals (_put_) _____ into effect.

3   Write a second sentence to follow each of those below, using the cues in brackets. The word or phrase in **bold** should be the centre of interest of the second sentence.

a) This town has suffered a great tragedy. (**ten people**, _kill, huge explosion, yesterday morning_) _Ten people were killed in a huge explosion_____ _yesterday morning._

b) Did you hear the news? (_from next week_, **all managers**, _give, 70 per cent pay rise_)

_____

c) Try these pills. (**they**, _must take, with water_)

_____

d) I see that play is on again. (_how many times_, **it**, _perform, before?_)

_____

e) The living room's going to be beautiful. (**it**, _decorate, at this moment_)

_____

Pronouns

Complete the following with a reflexive pronoun (e.g. _himself_), a possessive pronoun (e.g. _mine_) or an object pronoun (e.g. _me_).

a) Don't blame _yourself_ for what happened.

b) The team prides _____ on its appearance.

c) Come and sit next to _____.

d) She paid for the car _____.

e) Does he live by _____?

f) A: Is that magazine _____?
   B: Yes. Do you want to borrow _____?

Have (*get*) something done

Rewrite each sentence so that it means the same. Use *have* (*get*) *something done* where necessary.

a) He is going to cut the lawn for us on Sunday.
   We're going to have the lawn cut on Sunday.

b) Ben had the car painted last week.
   The garage *painted the car last week.*

c) The shop usually delivers the groceries for us.
   We _____

d) The stylist dyed Diane's hair red last week.
   Diane _____

e) Did you have your homework corrected?
   Did the teacher _____?

f) Have they cleaned your room yet?
   Have you _____?

g) At last they've had their shower installed.
   At last the plumber _____

VOCABULARY

Idiomatic expressions

Complete the idiomatic expressions below with words for parts of the body from the box.

| eyes leg foot hair hand tongue nose |
| head neck back |

a) Filling out tax forms is a pain in the
   ___neck___. I hate it.

b) Keep your _____ on! Don't panic!

c) You must be off your _____ going for a walk in this gale.

d) I'm putting my _____ down. I'm not going to let you go.

e) This party's getting wild. It's out of _____.

f) Stop making _____ at my husband!

g) I can't turn my _____ on him. He's always been kind to me.

h) Gill's so arrogant! She gets up my _____.

i) There's no evidence. He hasn't got a _____ to stand on.

j) Sorry! I meant to say 'Judy' – it was a slip of the _____ .

Newspaper headlines

Write down a word with a similar meaning from the headlines. Use a dictionary to help you if necessary.

Snow hits Xmas trains

MOTORWAY PLANS SHELVED

Food prices soar

BID TO HALT TAKE-OVER

Jobs axed at plant

JUDGE SLAMS TOP COMEDIAN

Government backs small companies

TOP TALKS BREAK DOWN

a) rise rapidly (*v*) ___soar___

b) supports (*v*) _____

c) attempt (*n*) _____

d) criticises (*v*) _____

e) causes problems for (*v*) _____

f) discussions (*n*) _____

g) cut without warning (*v*) _____

h) postponed (*v*) _____

WRITING

Letter of invitation

On a separate sheet of paper, rewrite this traditional wedding invitation as a semi-formal but friendly letter.

> *David and Marion Walters*
> *request the pleasure of the company of*
> ___Ms Jean Dennis___
> *at the marriage of their daughter*
> *Elizabeth*
> *with*
> *Mr Richard Mason*
> *at Woking Registry Office, Woking*
> *on Saturday, 12 July at 3 o'clock*
> *and afterwards at the Lamb Inn, Woking*
>
> *RSVP*
> *13 Holland Street, Merrow*

Mind your manners

LISTENING

1 [▭ 14.1] Listen to an extract from a radio programme about bad manners and tick the situations in the pictures which are referred to.

a) ___

b) ___

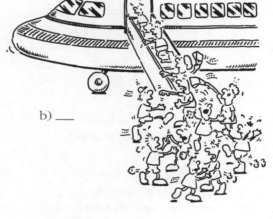

c) ___

d) ___

2 Listen again and complete the following examples of 'bad manners' according to the recording.

a) You hold a door open for someone and
   they don't thank you.

b) You are trying to pay in a _____ and
   _____

c) You are trying to get off a _____ and
   _____

d) You are trying to park your _____ and
   _____

e) People who eat _____
   _____ in the town.

f) Not saying _____

3 Answer the following questions.

a) When are old people as bad as young people?

   _____

   _____

b) In what way do people change when they become drivers?

   _____

   _____

GRAMMAR

Verb + object (+ *to*) + base form

Make a second sentence from the cues in brackets. Add other words such as articles and pronouns as necessary.

a) It was a poisonous snake. (*He / warn / me / not / touch / it*)
    He warned me not to touch it.

b) Jane came up to me at the party. (*She / invite / me / go to cinema*)
    _____

c) Helga's no good at this job. (*I / want / you / find / someone else*)
    _____

d) You look so lonely. (*It / make / me / feel / unhappy*)
    _____

e) I left the computer on last night. (*Remind / me / not / leave on / tonight*)
    _____

f) Spike doesn't like going to the cinema by himself. (*He / would like / you / go with him*)
    _____

g) The doctor said I was very tired. (*He order / me / take / month's rest*)
    _____

-ing or to?

1   Rewrite the sentences using an *-ing* clause or *to* + base form of the verb.

a) I think that we should give him a CD for his birthday.
    I suggest *giving him a CD for his birthday.*

b) Francisco said he hadn't stolen the money.
    Francisco denied _____

c) I imagine I'll see Paul this evening.
    I expect _____

d) Don't travel economy class on that airline!
    I advise you _____

e) I don't pay bills until I have to.
    I avoid _____

f) I know I put the money in my wallet.
    I remember _____

2   Complete the following sentences using an *-ing* form or *to* + base form of the verb in brackets.

a) That tyre's flat. It needs (*mend*) _____.

b) I thought I saw Sonia (*steal*) _____ a bike!

c) Will you show me how (*play*) _____ the violin?

d) Let's go (*ski*) _____ this Christmas.

e) Jessye waited for Wendy (*stop*) _____ (*play*) _____ the piano.

f) They are continuing (*make*) _____ good progress.

g) I'm interested in (*hear*) _____ what she has (*say*) _____.

h) His (*drive*) _____ is getting worse.

Expressing preferences

Look at the examples in the box and complete the sentences below with *prefer / would prefer* or *rather / would rather*.

> *I usually prefer watching TV to going to the theatre.*
> *I'd prefer (not) to read a book tonight.*
> *I'd have preferred (not) to have studied French when I was at school*
> *I'd rather (not) read a book tonight.*
> *I'd rather (not) have studied French when I was at school.*

a) I usually ___*prefer*___ listening to jazz to reading novels.

b) Which video would you _____ see?

c) I don't like this place, I would _____ to stay in a better hotel.

d) OK. Let's meet. But I _____ not talk about my past.

e) It was a boring party. I _____ have stayed in.

f) In future I _____ not to live by myself.

g) Do you _____ playing cards to listening to music?

VOCABULARY

Connotation

Write *P* for those words that normally have a positive connotation and *N* for those words that normally have a negative connotation.

a) stylish *P*

b) arrogant ___

c) easy-going ___

d) cowardly ___

e) efficient ___

f) boring ___

g) courageous ___

h) sexy ___

i) devious ___

j) greedy ___

k) hard-working ___

l) lazy ___

m) clever ___

Ambiguity

The word(s) in *italics* could have two meanings in context. Tick the two which are possible. Use a dictionary if necessary.

a) Tim's a very *curious* person.

   i)   eager to find out things ✓

   ii) new ___

   iii) strange ✓

b) She's very *fair*.

   i)   free from injustice ___

   ii) blonde-haired ___

   iii) pleasant ___

c) In France they drive on the *right* side of the road.

   i)   conventional ___

   ii) right-hand ___

   iii) correct ___

d) He *took advantage of* my knowledge of computers.

   i)   profited from ___

   ii) made unfair use of ___

   iii) disliked ___

e) It's very *cheap* furniture.

   i)   didn't cost a lot of money ___

   ii) brightly-coloured ___

   iii) low quality ___

f) *They are expected to be* here by seven.

   i)   They have been instructed to be ___

   ii) We think they will be ___

   iii) They are waiting for us here until ___

Proverbs

Complete the sentences with words from the box to make proverbs.

> iron   cat   policy   waters   eggs   rains
> actions   fonder   quarrel

a) Absence makes the heart grow ___*fonder*___.

b) Honesty is the best _____.

c) When the _____'s away the mice will play.

d) Don't put all your _____ in one basket.

e) It takes two to make a _____.

f) Still _____ run deep.

g) Strike while the _____'s hot.

h) _____ speak louder than words.

i) It never _____ but it pours.

WRITING

Spelling

Underline the correct spelling.

a) I can't *here/hear*.

b) He's *past/passed* his test.

c) *Its/It's* over *there/their*.

d) He's *quite/quiet* nice.

e) *Who's/Whose* is it?

f) Have you *red/read* it?

g) Who's your best *friend/freind*?

h) Tell me *wether/whether* you are coming tonight.

i) That's a very good *chioce/choice*.

• Training diets •

READING

1   Look at the picture and headline. Guess and underline the best alternative in the following sentences.

a) The woman is a *wrestler / the mother of the men / the wife of the men's boss.*

b) The headline means that *she is a very good wrestler / she is very strict with the men / women know more than men / she is in charge of the men.*

2   Read the text and underline things that the young wrestlers have to do and things they are not allowed to do as part of their discipline.

3   Write the numbers of the lines in the text which show or say the following.

a) What sometimes happens when the juniors get homesick. _55_

b) The 'Honoured Wife' is tougher than she seems. _____

c) In Japan Sumo is more than just a sport. _____

d) Champion wrestlers are famous and important. _____

4   Answer the following questions.

a) What two meanings could *no longer with us* have? (line 13)

_____

b) What emotions does the writer feel for the wrestlers? Give a reason.

_____

c) What does the phrase *a long, sharp shock* refer to? (line 39)

_____

d) Why is the stew *chanko nabe* important?

_____

e) Give three reasons why some newcomers lose weight.

_____

Mother's superior

'There must be strict discipline in a Sumo stable,' 'Honoured Wife' 47-year-old Noriko Fujishima told me primly as she perched like a tiny bird on a vast sofa in her mirrored drawing room in
5 Tokyo. 'In the wrestlers' dormitory the lights must be out at ten o'clock promptly! And the doors are locked so that they cannot get out again!

'In the past, it is true,' – 'Honoured Wife' could
10 scarcely bring herself to make this horrifying admission – 'we *did* have some bad ones who used to sneak out of a window after lights out. But they are no longer with us.' I dared not ask what 'no longer with us' meant.

15 I never thought I'd feel sorry for Sumo wrestlers: 22-stone hulks in the ring can inspire a variety of emotions, but pity isn't one of them.

At first glance 'Honoured Wife' is a sweet, delicate, giggly creature who looks as fragile as a
20 piece of porcelain but that's just the outer appearance. The inner reality is another matter.

Only her friends call her Noriko: to everyone else she is the Honoured Wife of the Boss of the Fujishima Stable, which owns, trains and houses
25 30 wrestlers, aged from 15 to 27.

Sumo wrestling now has a big following in Britain but in Japan it is not just a sport. Because of its ancient links with the Shinto religion – many of whose purification ceremonies are used
30 in the ring – Sumo has an almost sacred status in Japanese culture.

Champion Sumo wrestlers become millionaires, are fêted everywhere, showered with gifts by major business patrons and treated with all the
35 awe and adulation of pop stars. But a young wrestler entering a stable – so-called because their human livestock is treated as though they were a cross between prize race horses and gigantic schoolboys – is in for a long, sharp shock.

40 Apprentice wrestlers rise at dawn, perform all the household chores, work as valets to the highest-ranking wrestlers, endure fearsome workouts, *and* do all the cooking. Sumo food consists of a huge, bubbling stew called *chanko nabe*, an
45 ancient recipe to clothe a Sumo wrestler's bones in wads of highly-muscled fat.

Only two meals are taken a day, and the youngest wrestlers eat last, after the stable stars have their stomachs filled. 'To begin with, some of the
50 newcomers even lose weight as a result! They're not used to the work, and some don't like *chanko nabe*.'

'Yes, it's very hard for the juniors. They do get very lonely and homesick sometimes, so I have to
55 be their comforter. My husband, the Boss, is the one they must learn to fear: when he's around, they daren't even leave their slippers out of line.'

Does she ever allow her homesick hulks to phone home? 'Yes, I encourage that. Although, you
60 know, when a wrestler enters the stable his real mother always tells him that from that moment on, he must look on *me* as his real mother.'

(from *Male & Femail*)

VOCABULARY

Numbers

1 [📼 15.1]   Listen and write down what you hear. Write numbers and symbols. Do not write down words.

a) _____   f) _____
b) _____   g) _____
c) _____   h) _____ (*tennis*)
d) _____   i) _____ (*soccer*)
e) _____   j) _____ (*soccer*)

2   Write the following in words.

a) 240,000 _____
b) 14⅓ _____
c) 18 − 7 + 4 = 15 _____
d) £11.61 _____
e) 1993 (*year*) _____

Idioms

Complete the sentences with idioms from the box in the correct form. Use a dictionary to help you if necessary.

```
break the ice   close shave   in the dark
on the cards    pull strings   rings a bell
meet (someone) halfway
```

a) I know the manager well so I was able to
   _____*pull*_____ a few _____*strings*_____
   and get you the job.
b) His name _____ but I can't
   remember whether I've ever met him.
c) They're all being so formal. Let's play a game
   to _____.
d) I'll _____ you _____
   and pay £1,000 for that car but I won't pay
   £1,500.
e) That was a _____! That bus nearly
   hit us.
f) I think another price increase is _____
   very shortly.
g) Why are you so secretive? Why do you always
   keep me _____ about everything?

GRAMMAR

Quantity

1 Choose a word from the box to complete the phrases.

> tube jar packet bottle pile bunch
> tin loaf

a) a _____*bottle*_____ of milk

b) a _____ of bread

c) a _____ of flowers

d) a _____ of toothpaste

e) a _____ of cigarettes

f) a _____ of sardines

g) a _____ of books

h) a _____ of marmalade

2 One of the words or phrases in *italics* is countable, the other is uncountable. Underline the correct alternatives.

a) I'm going to get a new *job / work*.

b) She gave me some good *advice / suggestion*.

c) There's a lovely *chair / furniture* over there.

d) How much *luggage / suitcase* can you carry?

e) How many *pound coins / money* have you got?

f) That's very interesting *fact / information*.

Compounds of *some, any, no, every*

Complete the sentences with words from the box.

> somewhere everything no one anyone
> everywhere anything

a) If there's _____ I can do for you, just let me know.

b) I can't find my car. I've looked _____ for it.

c) There's _____ here apart from me.

d) Sylvia's _____ outside in the garden.

e) If _____ knows the answer, it will be John!

f) They left the bed but stole _____ else.

Each, another, both, either, etc.

Look at the picture and complete the sentences using words from the box and any other words that are necessary.

> all none another neither/nor both
> the other each either

a) _*Both of*_ the men __*are*__ wearing dark shorts.

b) The man doing the long jump hasn't got light hair. The man doing the pole vault hasn't _____.

c) _____ the woman throwing the javelin _____ the woman doing the high jump _____ dark hair.

d) _____ of the athletes _____ sitting down.

e) _____ of the athletes _____ wearing shorts.

f) One man has dark hair; _____ man has, too.

g) _____ woman _____ light hair.

h) The man on the left is doing the long jump. The man on the right is doing _____ sport.

PRONUNCIATION

Words with the same spelling

A word with the same spelling as another, but different in meaning, grammar or pronunciation, is called a homograph.

1 Write the words, using the Pronunciation chart on page 149 of the Students' Book to help you work out how they are spelt.

a) /ˈrekɔːd/   /rɪˈkɔːd/   _record_

b) /ˈmɪnɪt/   /maɪˈnjuːt/   _____

c) /wɪnd/   /waɪnd/   _____

d) /kənˈdʌkt/   /ˈkondʌkt/   _____

e) /lɪv/   /laɪv/   _____

f) /prɪˈzent/   /ˈprezənt/   _____

2 [📼 15.2] Listen to the recording and underline the transcribed words you hear in Exercise 1. The first one is done for you.

3 Complete the sentences using the underlined words from Exercise 1.

a) He got a prize for good _____.

b) I don't think this will _____ a problem.

c) Will you _____ the football match tonight on your video?

d) The _____ is very strong today.

e) Ugh! Look! A real _____ snake!

f) I won't be a _____.

WRITING

Punctuation

Look at the extracts from a student newspaper. Correct the errors according to the editorial cues in brackets.

a)
> professor jones was last seen in hyde park in november.

(*capital letters*)

b)
> Wheres your newspapers principles?

(*apostrophes*)

c)
> Add the fish oysters and herbs followed by the tomato.

(*commas*)

d)
> It was lucky I discovered her, said Mr Biggs.

(*speech marks*)

e)
> dr jones lecturer in philosophy at kings college said im looking forward to the day when this college listens to students views

(*punctuation*)

Lists

On a separate sheet of paper, write down the ingredients for your favourite recipe. Then make a shopping list of the things you will need to prepare the recipe. You might need to use abbreviations such as the following:
kg (*kilo*), g (*gram*), tsp (*teaspoon*), tbs (*tablespoon*).

A deafening noise

LISTENING

1 [🎞 16.1] Listen to Helen, Dick and Chris and write down the number of the picture which illustrates the sport they are talking about.

a) Helen: *2*

b) Dick: _____

c) Chris: _____

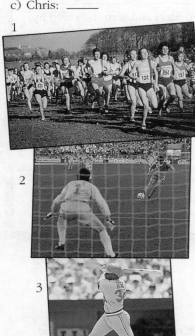

1

2

3

2 Write down in note form *one* reason why the person talking likes the sport.

a) Football: *easy to work out what's going on*

b) Marathon running: _____

_____

c) Baseball: _____

_____

3 Answer these questions according to the texts.

a) What is one of the most exciting moments in a football match?

_____

b) What is more important: getting a goal or the way the goal is scored?

_____

c) What is one thing that contributes to the atmosphere of a baseball game?

_____

d) When can baseball seem very slow?

_____

e) When does a fielder have to catch a ball over his shoulder?

_____

f) Why does Chris like to watch the strugglers?

_____

VOCABULARY

Word building

Complete the following table, using your dictionary where necessary. In some cases there may be more than one possibility.

Adjective	Adverb	Noun	Verb
exciting	*excitingly*	*excitement*	excite
	argumentatively		
educational			
		legality	
	reasonably		
embarrassing			
			think
		fantasy	
decisive			
			accuse

Similes

1 A simile is an expression which describes one thing directly comparing it with another. (Example: *He's **as deaf as a post**.*)
Match the words in column A with the phrases in column B.

A	**B**
a) as good	1 as a feather
b) as keen	2 as a whistle
c) as old	3 as mustard
d) as white	4 as a cucumber
e) as quick	5 as the hills
f) as cool	6 as gold
g) as clean	7 as a knife
h) as light	8 as a flash
i) as sharp	9 as a sheet

(a connected to 6)

2 Complete the sentences with one of the similes from Exercise 1.

a) He answered her question *as quick as a flash*.

b) I've heard that story before. It's _____

_____.

c) He never panics in a crisis. He's _____

_____.

d) Those old cups have been washed well. They're _____

_____.

e) She's got a very quick mind. She's _____

_____.

f) When she saw her ex-husband she went

_____.

g) Tim's very enthusiastic. He's _____

_____.

h) Your children are so well-behaved. They're

_____.

i) It's very delicate. Pick it up. It's _____

_____.

Foreign words and phrases

Some foreign words and phrases are used in English, keeping their original spelling and much of their original identity. Complete the sentences with words and phrases from the box. Use a dictionary to help you.

> status quo pro rata cul-de-sac bon voyage
> macho faux pas blasé vice versa siesta
> ad nauseam incognito

a) When you get famous you get very *blasé* _____ about money.

b) The school fees were reduced _____ because he missed the first half of term.

c) She changed her appearance because she was travelling _____.

d) I think I'll have a short _____ after lunch.

e) He thinks he's very tough, very _____, but underneath he's soft.

f) The Government won't make changes. It wants to keep the _____.

g) We've heard that record _____. Turn it off!

h) Bye! _____, and give us a call when you get there!

i) When he wants to stay in, she wants to go out, and _____.

j) You never get any through-traffic down this road. It's a _____.

k) He committed a terrible _____ when he called the Queen 'Darling'.

GRAMMAR

Modals

Complete the sentences in the affirmative or the negative, according to the cues in brackets, using the modals from the box. In some cases there is more than one possibility.

| must should may will ('ll) can |

a) Don't worry! I *'ll*_____ be back in a couple of hours. (*promise – certainty*)

b) Sue's yawning a lot. She _____ be very tired. (*near certainty*)

c) They're having a baby. They _____ have to buy a bigger house. (*possibility*)

d) I don't think you _____ go swimming immediately after lunch. It's very bad for you. (*advice*)

e) That _____ be Takumi. It's too early for him to be here. (*impossibility*)

f) _____ I have a word with you? It's very important. (*permission*)

g) Claudia _____ walk because she's got a very bad back. (*lack of ability*)

h) You _____ drink and drive. It's against the law. (*prohibition*)

Reference words

Read the text and say who or what the words in *italics* refer to.

. . . Deirdre Fount remembered the terrible sports days and open days and school concerts, when (1) *her* mother would bear down upon everyone, keeping hold of (2) *her* daughter's hand, patting her on (3) *the* shoulder. (4) *She* used to ask prying questions of teachers and pupils, and wear appalling hats. The memory of (5) *those* afternoons was acutely painful. And (6) *it* came back now because that afternoon she herself had wanted very much to go and meet (7) *her* son James from school, it had been with that idea in her mind that she had abandoned the accounts and gone out of the house. She wanted to walk with him down the avenue and have him tell her interesting things about (8) *his* day, and Westbourne should see (9) *them* together and say, 'There is Mrs Deirdre Fount and her growing (10) *son*. How well they look together!'

(from *A Change for the Better* by Susan Hill)

1 ____*Deirdre*____	6 _____
2 _____	7 _____
3 _____	8 _____
4 _____	9 _____
5 _____	10 _____

WRITING

Dialogue of complaint

On a separate sheet of paper, write a telephone dialogue between a hotel receptionist (A) and a guest (B) using the framework below.

| A | Answer the phone. |

| | B | Complain that your television isn't working. |

| A | Apologise, giving a reason for not being able to do anything. |

| | B | Try to persuade the receptionist to do something. |

| A | Refuse politely, giving another reason. |

| | B | Get angry and ask to speak to the manager. |

| A | Refuse politely, making an excuse. |

| | B | Insist on changing rooms. |

| A | Make a promise. |

| | B | Respond to the promise. |

• Staying alive •

LISTENING

You are going to listen to Simon Bates, a well-known radio presenter in Britain, talking to some people on the telephone about their opinions of fox-hunting. The title of the radio programme is *The unspeakable in pursuit of the uneatable*. The first person he talks to is a hunt saboteur (someone who tries to stop hunts taking place). He also talks to a farmer and a young girl who has taken part in hunts.

1 [🔊 17.1]   Listen to the recording and tick the arguments which the hunt saboteur uses.

a) One of our aims is to help the animals who are being killed. ____

b) The hunters kill for pleasure. ____

c) Very few chickens are free-range. ____

d) Hunting is out-dated and should be stopped. ____

e) Foxes are not harmful to farmers' jobs. ____

2 [🔊 17.2]   Listen and tick the arguments which the farmer uses.

a) Hunting is an enjoyable sport. ____

b) Foxes are a danger to sheep. ____

c) Foxes should all be killed. ____

d) Hunting is the kindest way of killing foxes. ____

e) Field sports help the landscape. ____

3 [🔊 17.3]   Listen and answer the following.

a) When did Felicia start hunting?

_____

b) What happened on her first hunt that made her dislike hunting?

_____

c) Why did her uncle wipe blood on her?

_____

d) How does she feel about hunting now?

_____

Vocabulary in context

Look at the quotations from the recordings and replace the words in *italics* with a word or expression from the box.

kindest	plants grown by farmers
big help	very unpleasant
animals kept on a farm	illegal
animals that kill or eat other animals	

a) 'The particular practices in question are so *obnoxious* (_____) that there must come a time when they will become *outlawed* (_____).'

b) 'There's a need to control wild animals that damage *crops* (_____) and *livestock* (_____).'

c) 'Under those circumstances foxes are actually a *boon* (_____) to the farmer.'

d) 'We do suffer from *predators* (_____), in particular the fox.'

e) 'Hunting is the *most humane* (_____) way of exercising control.'

61

GRAMMAR

Reported speech

Read this interview with someone who enjoys hunting foxes, and change it into reported speech.

I: Why do you hunt?

H: Hunting is a marvellous way of relaxing, and I love the countryside. I went on my first hunt when I was six but took it up seriously when I was sixteen. Hunting is part of the rule of nature.

I: Is hunting a cruel way to kill foxes?

H: It's the only humane way – the fox either gets away or dies in seconds.

a) I asked her _____

b) She told me that _____ way
_____ the countryside.
She said that _____
_____ six, but _____
_____. She
commented that hunting _____
_____

c) I wanted to know _____

d) She replied that _____
humane way because _____
seconds.

Direct speech

Read the report of an interview with a hunt saboteur. On a separate sheet of paper, write the dialogue that took place. Include the appropriate punctuation.

I asked a saboteur what sabotaging a hunt involved.
'*What does sabotaging a hunt involve? I asked.*

She replied that that week they had been working in groups of about fifteen people. Their aim was to make sure that the fox stayed alive, and didn't get caught.

I wanted to know exactly what they did, and she explained that they blew horns to confuse the hounds and sat on gates so the hunt couldn't pass.

Reporting verbs

1 Complete the following sentences which all follow the same verb pattern.

a) 'Remember to take your keys, Max'.
Karen reminded _____

b) 'If I were you I'd wait until tomorrow,' Sue told me.
Sue advised _____

c) 'Come to dinner next Friday,' she said to us.
She invited _____

d) 'Don't go out in the car. It's really icy,' he said to her.
He warned _____

e) 'Get out of my office this minute!' my boss said to me.
My boss ordered _____

f) 'The party will be great fun.! You must come!' Louisa told us.
Louisa persuaded _____

2 Complete the sentences using the verbs from the box. All the sentences follow different patterns.

accuse complain congratulate offer apologise suggest

a) 'Well done, David. You've won first prize!'
Tom _____

b) 'I'm sure you scratched my car yesterday, Tim.'
Jenny _____

c) 'Why don't we go in my car?' said Steve.
Steve _____

d) 'We're sorry we're late,' they said.
They _____

e) 'Let me get you a drink,' Jessica said to us.
Jessica _____

f) 'That test wasn't fair,' the students said.
The students _____

VOCABULARY

Adjectives and nouns

Put the nouns from the box next to the adjectives with which they can be associated in the list below. In all cases there is more than one possibility.

> paper   food   weather   pullover   bed
> drink   cheese   wine   ticket   book

a) plain _____ *paper   food   pullover* _____

b) single _____

c) hot _____

d) dry _____

e) thick _____

f) strong _____

Synonyms and antonyms

1   Write down a word which has a similar meaning to the one in *italics*.

a) a *nice* experience _____ *pleasant* _____

b) a *funny* film _____

c) a *difficult* exam _____

d) a *hot* curry _____

e) an *easy* decision _____

f) a *brave* man _____

g) a *talkative* student _____

h) a *wonderful* meal _____

i) a *rich* country _____

j) an *untidy* room _____

2   Write down a word which has the opposite meaning in context to the one in italics.

a) a *weak* character _____ *strong* _____

b) *strong* cigarettes _____

c) a *married* person _____

d) a *single* ticket _____

e) a *hard* chair _____

f) a *loud* voice _____

g) *sour* grapes _____

h) *sweet* wine _____

i) *deep* water _____

j) a *light* sleeper _____

Phrasal verbs

Some phrasal verbs are formed with a verb + adverb participle + preposition. Example: *I'm putting in for a pay rise (put in for* means 'to make a formal request for').
Rewrite the following sentences, replacing the words in *italics* with the phrasal verbs from the box.

> get through to   get out of   get on with
> run out of   put up with   get away with (it)

a) I won't *tolerate* your behaviour any more.

_____

b) *Continue with* your work.

_____

c) It's very difficult to *reach* you by phone.

_____

d) Don't cheat because you won't *escape without being punished*.

_____

e) I'll try to *avoid the duty of* going to see my relatives this weekend.

_____

f) We have*n't got any more* coffee. Can you nip to the shops?

_____

WRITING

Personal letter

Write a letter to your friend Rachel following the outline below.

a) Write your address and date.
b) Thank her for the birthday present she sent you and say why you liked it.
c) Tell her about what you and the family did on your holidays, anything funny which happened, the people you met, etc.
d) Suggest that you meet in London one day. Suggest what you might do, see, etc. Offer to pick her up.
e) Finish the letter by sending love to the family.

Rites of passage

READING

1 Read the text and write *T* (for *True*) or *F* (for *False*) next to the following statements.

a) Silvermere Haven is the only pet cemetery in the London area. _____

b) Michael used to be a company director. _____

c) He went into business with some vets. _____

d) He is not allowed to bury bigger animals.

_____

e) Burial is more expensive than cremation.

_____

f) Pam has learned to be unemotional.

_____

2 Read the text again and answer the following questions.

a) What kind of people get very upset at losing their pets?

_____

b) How many people have got a plot for their pet at Silvermere?

_____

c) What kind of things do owners bury with their pets?

_____

d) What do the owners do with the ashes if they take them away?

_____

e) What do visitors do on a Sunday afternoon?

_____

f) What kind of thing does Michael regard as 'commercialised'?

_____

In Loving Memory of Bonzo

As owners of Silvermere Haven, the biggest pet cemetery in the London area, Pam and Michael Gilbert are used to seeing grown men and women speechless with sorrow and stunned by losing their pet. They know that losing an animal can devastate even the strongest people.

"They go to pieces sometimes," said Michael. And so they turn a considerate blind eye as the owners contemplate a life without Bonzo, or Worthington Bear, who "has gone for long walkies". Michael, ex-company director, began the 'business' just over a year ago, quite by chance. "Our cat Elsie was getting on a bit – she was about 13 – and rather ill. I told the vet that my wife would go mad if anything happened to her but was quite interested to know what he did with pets bodies after they'd died. 'Don't you know?' he said. 'Most of them get boiled down and made into by-products.'

"Well, I was horrified! There are about 70 vets within a 12-mile range of here and I told him that I was surprised that none of them had got together to make a little cemetery. Apparently, he had talked about doing it with his colleagues for years, but nobody seemed to have the ground – or the time.

"I became completely set on the idea and said 'Right, I'll go ahead and do it on my own'."

Since then, about 200 pet-owners have found a plot and peace of mind at Silvermere. "The council stressed that they were only giving us permission to bury small household pets. I think they were a little afraid that people would come along dragging giraffes, tigers or elephants. We wouldn't want to bury large animals anyway – it would be totally impractical."

So while faithful Dobbin meets his traditional end at the knacker's yard, the privileged cats and dogs at Silvermere enter whatever animal afterlife there might be complete with special blankets, pillows and toys.

Cremation is cheaper than burial, because most owners prefer to take the ashes away, and therefore don't need a plot.

"Sometimes they sprinkle them around here," said Michael. "Or in their back gardens, or where, in the case of dogs, they used to take them for their favourite walk."

A battered car drove solemnly into the car park. As father began a bleak procession to the crematorium, holding the late family dog in his arms, emotions were clearly running high. How did Pam cope and offer comfort to the bereaved?

"I'm afraid I don't. I'm terrible. They cry and I start crying. Even over the phone. They've only got to mention their names – like Mr Snowball – and I'm off."

Sunday afternoon is a time when most visitors come – some for miles – to plant shrubs, push flowers into jam jars and reflect on the time when little Yogi used to chew slippers and chase the milkman.

Besides the picture book setting and yearning for a plot one's pet can call his own, what must also attract customers to Silvermere is its complete lack of commercial urgency. If owners want to get coffins made to measure or bring their dog's body up from Bournemouth in a taxi that is completely up to them. Ordinary burials start at £8 for a cat to £25 for an extra large dog (less for a cremation).

"We hate the idea of becoming all commercialised like the Americans," said Michael. "I don't think anybody wants a burial service, or organ music. After all, the British like to do things in a quiet, civilised way . . ."

(from *The Sunday Times Magazine*, © Times Newspapers Limited)

Glossary

Bonzo: a typical name for a dog in Britain.
Worthington Bear/Yogi/Mr Snowball: unusual dogs' names
Dobbin: a traditional name for a horse
knacker's yard: the place where old horses go to be killed

GRAMMAR

Defining relative clauses

1 Complete these quiz questions by adding a relative pronoun.

a) What's the name of the 100 metre sprinter _____ lost a gold medal because he failed a drugs test?

b) What's the common name of the substance _____ is known as sodium chloride?

c) What's the name of the actor _____ performance in *Rain man* won him an Oscar?

d) What's the name of the part of the Atlantic Ocean _____ many boats and planes are said to have mysteriously disappeared?

e) Can you explain the reason _____ very little red wine is produced in Britain?

2 Answer the questions and then check your answers on the last page of the book.

Defining and non-defining relative clauses

Join these sentences together with relative pronouns. If the information is not essential to the sentence, add commas.

a) Sir David Lovall was speaking at the meeting last night. He is a politician.
   Sir David Lovall, who is a politician, was speaking at the meeting last night.

b) The shop is having a sale. I buy all my clothes there.

c) Pauline was telling me about her eldest daughter. She lives in Australia.

d) I need the newspaper. I threw it away last night.

e) Kate is coming to stay for Christmas. Her son is married to my cousin.

Participle clauses

Change the verb in brackets to either a present or a past participle.

a) They eventually found him (*listen*) __listening__ to music in the attic.

b) The protestors marched down the street (*wave*) _____ banners.

c) The two people (*injure*) _____ in the accident are still in a critical condition.

d) The town (*choose*) _____ for the next Olympics was one nobody had expected.

e) Not (*want*) _____ to create a scene, she waited until her husband was on his own before shouting at him.

f) The man (*send*) _____ to repair my TV was useless.

g) I can hear something (*move*) _____ downstairs.

Adjectives ending in -*ing* and -*ed*

Underline the correct alternatives.

a) Anna was really *disappointing/disappointed* when she couldn't get tickets for the show.

b) I felt very *confused/confusing* by the explanation.

c) William felt really *embarrassing/embarrassed* when he realised he had left his money at home.

d) Chloe finds his jokes quite *amusing/amused* but I must admit I am *boring/bored* by them.

e) Armando was *annoying/annoyed* with his son when he realised he had lost his football boots again.

f) Belinda looks very *satisfying/satisfied* with herself – as if she's done something very clever.

g) The state of the economy is really *worrying/worried* at the moment.

VOCABULARY

Word building

Complete each sentence with a noun, verb or an adjective formed from the word in brackets.

a) I'm sure he'll do well. He's extremely (*ambition*) _____.

b) Did you know the boss had handed in his (*resign*) _____?

c) The only problem is that she's not very (*patience*) _____.

d) The skirt's too short. I'd better (*long*) _____ it.

e) Did you understand the teacher's (*explain*) _____?

f) It's a nice house, but we'd need to (*modern*) _____ the kitchen.

g) The beach was too (*crowd*) _____ so we went for a drive.

h) You may need to (*hot*) _____ that soup up.

i) The train has been cancelled because of engine (*fail*) _____.

Prepositional phrases

Complete the sentences with the prepositions from the box.

for under by on in

a) Did you hear the programme _____ the radio last night?

b) Do you want to pay _____ cheque?

c) Come round _____ a drink later on.

d) I think the problem is still _____ discussion.

e) Richard is away _____ business this week.

f) Have you read the new book _____ Martin Amis?

g) Gillian, it's Yvonne _____ the phone.

h) Shall we go _____ a quick walk before dinner?

i) The doorman is _____ orders not to let anyone in.

j) Please fill in this form _____ black ink.

Confusing words

Underline the correct alternatives.

a) Today is their silver *wedding/marriage* anniversary.

b) She invited all her *parents/relatives* to her party.

c) What are you going to *dress/wear* this evening?

d) Do you know what time the train *arrives/reaches* Glasgow?

e) Germany *won/beat* Brazil by three goals.

f) I've offered a *prize/reward* for anyone finding my cat.

g) Could you *take/bring* my coat here, please?

h) It was a wonderful *possibility/opportunity* and she took it.

i) The coat didn't *fit/suit* me – it was too big.

j) A: What are your hobbies?

B: Well, I *do/practise* quite a lot of sports.

PRONUNCIATION

Vowel sounds

On a separate sheet of paper, copy the vowel sounds below. Put the words in the box in the correct group, according to their sounds. There should be three words in each group.

people	pool	uncle	could	bury	build
lawn	aunt	match	fur	cough	young	if
move	book	health	can't	piece	bought
fill	watch	earth	tap	wheel	horse	does
word	stood	any	half	bottle	juice	can

/iː/
people ____

/ʊ/
____

/e/
____

/ʌ/
____

/ɒ/
____

/æ/
____

/uː/
____

/ɑː/
____

/ɔː/
____

/ɪ/
____

/ɜː/
____

WRITING

Joining sentences

1 Complete the sentences with words and expressions from the box.

both until during whenever by the time in case unless

a) _____ I go out without an umbrella it always rains.

b) I had to wait two hours _____ the consultant was available.

c) Take some change _____ you need it for the phone.

d) _____ Andrea and Paul love jazz.

e) I'll be there at 7 _____ the bus is late.

f) _____ they got home he had fallen asleep in the chair.

g) My husband was fast asleep _____ the first half of the film.

2 Rewrite the two sentences as one sentence on a separate sheet of paper, using each of the joining words in the box once.

while unless although whereas so even though after because

a) We were both very unfit. Nevertheless, we decided to enter for the marathon.
   We decided to enter for the marathon, although we were both very unfit.

b) She had left her purse at home. That was why I lent her £5.

c) I didn't have any breakfast. As a result, I was starving all morning.

d) Adrian is very tall. In contrast, his sister is tiny.

e) They bought a new house. Then they decided to go abroad.

f) I looked everywhere for the letter. Meanwhile, the phone was ringing non-stop.

g) Stay in bed and keep warm. Otherwise you won't get better.

h) I really hate the idea of seafood. However, I'm going to try it.

• A mystery •

READING 1

1   Read the first part of the story *Skeleton in the cupboard* by Tony Wilmot and answer the following questions.

a) Who are the two main characters?

_____

b) How did they meet each other?

_____

He was watching the park gates from his usual bench by the pond. The girl would soon be joining him for her mid-day break.

For several days now they had sat at the
5 same bench and exchanged pleasantries after she had laughed at the way the ducks fought over the crusts he had thrown to them. She was twenty-ish, and attractive, but he did not flatter himself that her interest was in any way
10 physical. He subscribed to the adage 'No fool like an old fool'. Besides, he was more than twice her age.

To him it was a harmless flirtation – a fillip to his middle-aged man's morale – and he had
15 found himself looking forward to their lunchtime meetings.

Earlier that morning, however, events had taken a more serious turn. The girl had paid a visit to the Vehicle Registration Department in
20 the Town Hall.

His secretary had come into his office. 'There's a young lady here, Mr Smythe, asking if we keep records of car ownership . . . MG sports cars in particular. I said I thought not.'
25 He had felt a twinge of unease at the mention of the car type. 'Quite so,' he had replied. 'Tell her registrations are all on the national computer now. In any case, we couldn't give out that kind of information.'
30 He had peered at the reception desk through his office's glass partition. The enquirer was the girl from the park bench. An odd co-incidence, he had thought. Or was it something more?

35 Now, as she entered the park gates with that long stride and purposeful expression, his unease returned.

'Hello – we meet again,' she said, sitting beside him.
40 'Ah, yes . . . sky looks a bit overcast. Hope we aren't in for some rain.' He gestured at the apple she was peeling with a penknife. 'Lunch?'

'Yes, worse luck. I'm on a diet.'

He smiled. 'You seem to be here most days.
45 Do you work hereabouts?'

'Oh no. In fact, I don't live here. I'm just staying in town while I'm doing some research. I'm from Elmston, actually.'

'Really? I know Elmston . . .' he began. The
50 words were out before the warning bell rang. 'Well, I don't exactly know it . . . pal of mine . . . knew him years ago . . . used to live there. Is this your first visit here?'

'Yes.'
55 'Nice place.' he said. 'Bit dull, though.'

'Not at all. It's charming.'

'What are you researching? Our town's chequered history, perhaps? Parts date from the Roman occupation.'
60 'How interesting. But no – I'm trying to trace someone.'

'Ah! Bit of detective work?'

She smiled. 'In a way. I'm beginning to find out what a job it is tracing someone who may
65 not want to be traced. No wonder the police have to spend so much time on investigations.'

'And the "trail" has led from Elmston to here?'

'Indirectly, yes. But I've had to spend time
70 in several places first. I'm hoping this will be the last.'

'Sounds very intriguing,' he said, hoping to entice her to reveal more without seeming to be prying into her private life.

75 'I suppose it is, in a way. I'm going back more than twenty years, though.' She made a wry face. 'Which is setting myself a difficult task.'

'I don't suppose you were even born then?'
80 he said.

'I was – just! Anyway, I've managed to unearth a few clues. The person I'm looking for had an MG sports car then and got married during the same period. I know it's a bit of a
85 long shot, but it might just pay off.'

His unease became a shiver which set him on edge even more. He was like a rabbit hypnotised by the snake, wanting to get away but unable to move. 'But I mustn't bore you
90 with my personal affairs,' she went on. 'What about you? What line of business are you in?'

'Oh, nothing much. Civil servant, actually. Quite dull, I'm afraid. I wish I could be an 007 like you but . . . I'm just a nine-to-five chap.'

95 'Don't be so modest. There's nothing wrong with being a civil servant.'

He made a deprecating gesture but inwardly he was thrilled that a pretty girl was finding him interesting enough to want to flirt
100 with him.

'Married, of course?'

He was on the point of saying no when he noticed her glance at the ring on his left hand. He nodded.

105 'The dishy men always are! Lived here long, have you?'

He did not like the turn the conversation was taking. 'Oh, quite some time.' He made a show of checking his wristwatch.

110 'Well, I must be getting back. I, er . . . that is, perhaps we might see each other again tomorrow?'

'Yes, let's. About one o'clock?'

He said that would be fine.

2   Read the text again and find the following information.

a) Where and when do the man and woman meet?

_____

b) How long have they known each other?

_____

c) How old is the girl?

_____

d) How old is the man?

_____

e) Why is the girl in Elmston?

_____

f) What is the man's job?

_____

3   Answer the following questions.

a) What do you think is the significance of the phrase *a warning bell rang?* (line 50)

_____

b) What do you think *a nine-to-five chap* is? (line 94)

_____

c) *He didn't like the turn the conversation was taking.* (line 107) What turn was the conversation taking, and why didn't he like it?

_____

d) A *skeleton in the cupboard* (which is the title of the story) is a shocking fact from the past that someone often keeps secret. The man has one. What do you think it is?

_____

Vocabulary in context

Find words or phrases in the text with the same meaning as the following.

a) hard surface of bread (line 7 *noun*) _____

b) behaviour which attracts sexual interest or attention (line 13 *noun*) _____

c) moved his hands (line 41 *verb*) _____

d) find (line 60 *verb*) _____

e) very interesting (line 72 *adjective*) _____

f) finding out about private things (line 74 *verb*)

_____

LISTENING 1

1 [📼 19.1]   Listen to the next part of the story.

a) Read this summary of the recording in which one mistake is underlined. Then underline ten more mistakes.

Robert Smythe went home from work <u>two hours</u> early because he had a lot of work to do at home. He looked at two newspaper cuttings in a metal box which he kept in his bedroom. Twenty years ago he had killed a six-year-old girl while he was driving to Margaret's parents house, who lived near Elmston. He had been driving an MG sports car. He knew the road well and was driving slowly but the road was wet and his brakes were not good. He didn't see the girl, who was not on a pedestrian crossing. He didn't stop because he had just been given a new job, and he had just got married. Nobody saw the accident or heard his brakes.

    Robert thought that the girl in the park was a policewoman, who was looking for him.

b) Write the correct sentences on a separate sheet of paper. Example:
He went home an hour early.

2   Circle the correct definition of the word or expression from the text.

a) in a *leafy* suburb on the outskirts of town
   i) dirty   (ii) with lots of trees

b) Inside the box were two *yellowing* clippings
   i) very old   ii) frightening

c) for the *umpteenth* time
   i) large number of   ii) first

d) traffic had been *diverted*
   i) stopped   ii) sent in a different direction

e) he'd *skipped* a service to save money
   i) decided not to have checks on his car
   ii) forgotten to put petrol in his car

f) He *pecked away* (at his food)
   i) ate very little   ii) ate hungrily

g) The police enquiries had no doubt *fizzled out*
   i) become more urgent   ii) stopped

h) far more pressing cases *on their plate*
   i) to investigate   ii) to eat

READING 2

1   Read the next part of the story and complete the following information.

a) The girl said she had found _____ and a _____ of the car.

b) Robert said he had _____ from Elmston who _____.

c) He asked her for her _____ _____ so that he _____ if he found _____.

d) The girl stopped at a _____ where she collected a _____.

e) She then went into the offices of the _____ _____ to look for _____.

f) Robert lost sight of her later because _____ _____.

That night he hardly slept. At the office next day he clockwatched until it was time to go to the park. The girl was already there when he arrived.

5   'I was hoping I'd see you today,' she said. 'You see, I'm certain I've come to the right town. You know I mentioned an MG . . . well, how's this for amateur sleuthing? . . . There's the car's number.'

10   A muscle in his cheek began to twitch rapidly as he read what was in her notebook. His MG's number. But how had she . . . ? The newspaper report said there had been no eyewitnesses.

15   'I'm missing the middle one or two digits in the number-plate, but it's enough.'

   'Very cloak-and-daggerish,' he said, forcing a smile. 'Have you tried the local Vehicle Registration Department? Perhaps they can

20   help.'

   'Oh yes. No luck, though. But guess what – I've got a photograph of the car.'

   The park seemed to spin. He gripped the bench with both hands.

25   'You all right?' she asked.

   'What? Oh yes. Just a twinge of indigestion.'

   'Well, I haven't actually got the photo-graph,' she went on. 'I've only seen the negative. I'm having a ten-by-eight print done

30   from it.'

'You have been busy!' His voice sounded unreal. 'Look, that friend of mine from Elmston. I've just remembered. *He* had an MG. He could be who you are looking for . . . I might still
35 have an address for him at home
. . . Have you got a phone number where I can contact you? Better still, an address in case I miss you here tomorrow.'
She wrote down both in her notebook and
40 tore the pages out for him. 'Now I must be off,' she said. 'I've got more sleuthing to do. I'll look out for you here again tomorrow.'
He gave her a minute or two's start then began to follow her. Her first stop was at a
45 photographic shop near the main square. She came out carrying a large buff-coloured envelope. He kept about fifty yards behind as she crossed the town centre to the offices of the *Evening Gazette*.
50 He followed her through the revolving doors, keeping the public newspaper stands in the foyer between himself and the point where she was talking at the enquiry counter.
Pretending to leaf through the week's back
55 numbers, he could hear snatches of conversation above the din of typewriters and telephones.
'. . . wedding report twenty-one years ago . . . would it be possible to . . .'
60 '. . . the archives are on the fourth floor . . . first door on the left as you come out of the lift . . .'
He watched the girl take the lift. Time passed. People came and went. He felt clammy
65 and conspicuous.
Eventually she reappeared out of the lift. The receptionist smiled. Had she found what she had been looking for?
Yes, she had.
70 He was in a cold sweat now, but he had no difficulty keeping her in sight, for he knew the town like the back of his hand. Where would she head next? Oh God, he thought, don't let it be the police station.
75 'Robert! Long time no see!' He started. It was a man he knew from the Parks Department. He felt like a schoolboy caught playing truant. 'Stretching your legs, eh, Robert?'
'Oh, er, yes.' He could see the girl dis-
80 appearing down a side turning. 'Popped out for some cigarettes.'
The man was grinning. 'Some looker, eh?'
'What?'

'That girl you were staring at.'
85 'Oh.' He forced a smile. 'Look, can't stop now. Let's have a drink next week. I'll ring you.'
When he finally got away, the girl was nowhere to be seen. He spent the rest of the
90 afternoon fretting at his desk. Whose wedding had she looked up? And why?

2 Answer the following questions.

a) Why do you think Robert is inventing the story about a friend with an MG?

He might _____

_____

b) What do you think is in the *large buff-coloured envelope*?

It must be _____

_____

c) Whose wedding had she been looking up?

She may _____

_____

d) What do you think Robert's colleague thought he was doing?

He must _____

_____

3 Replace the words in *italics* from the text with a similar word or expression.

a) He *gripped* the bench with both hands. (line 23)

_____

b) I must *be off* (line 40)

_____

c) Pretending to *leaf through* the week's back numbers. (line 54)

_____

d) *snatches* of conversation . . . (line 55)

_____

e) above the *din* of typewriters (line 56)

_____

f) he knew the town *like the back of his hand*. (line 72)

_____

LISTENING 2

1 [🔊 19.2]   Listen to the next part of the story and say what relevance the following have to the story.

a) A framed photo on the television.

_____

b) A photo of Margaret and Robert leaving to go on honeymoon.

_____

c) A balding man with a moustache.

_____

d) A 'Just married' placard.

_____

e) The electoral roll (the list of names and addresses of all those people who can vote in an area).

_____

f) *The Swan* (the name of a pub).

_____

g) A gin and tonic.

_____

2   What does Robert think the girl must have done? Use the cues to write sentences.

a) go to every photographer / find negatives

_____

b) got a print / negative

_____

c) search newspapers / for copy of photo and parents' addresses

_____

3   Why can't the girl have found the addresses of Margaret and Robert's parents?

_____

4   What excuse does Robert make for calling on the girl?

_____

5   What do you think will happen next?

_____

READING 3

Read the final part of the story and answer the following questions.

a) Who was the letter from?

_____

b) What is Margaret's 'skeleton'?

_____

c) How do you think Robert feels when he finds out?

_____

At the breakfast table next morning Margaret thought Robert looked pale and drawn; there were dark rings round his eyes and he seemed unusually preoccupied. Clearly he needed a holiday; he was working far too hard at that office.

She knew it probably would not be much good urging him to take the day off but she decided to try; to her surprise, he agreed.

'I do have a bit of a migraine, love,' he said.

'The rest will do you good. I'll ring the office and tell them you're not well.'

The 'plop' on the mat inside the front door told her the post had arrived. 'I'll go,' she said.

Two letters. One was Robert's bank statement, the other was for her. An unfamiliar handwriting.

She tore it open on her way back to the kitchen. It was a three-page letter, with a snapshot. The sudden shock, as she began to read, made her giddy.

. . . all I had to go on was your maiden name . . . you'd be surprised how many Margarets with that surname have got married since I was born . . . it meant checking each one to find if it was the right Margaret . . .

She stared at the attractive, fair-haired girl in the snap. Could it be . . . after all these years? It was something she had buried in her memory, something she had thought would remain buried; but, deep down, hadn't she always known she would never be able to escape from her past?

. . . when I first learned the truth about myself I was hurt and angry . . . but now that I'm grown up myself, I'm able to understand why you did what you did . . .

She sat at the table and rested her hands on the scrubbed pine to stop them trembling. She glanced at Robert but he seemed unaware of her agitation.

. . . finally traced you through your marriage to Robert Smythe . . . and now I feel I must meet you . . . of course, my adoptive parents will always be 'Mum' and 'Dad' to me but . . .

Blinking back the tears she heard Robert asking if the letter was bad news.

'Bad? Oh no . . .' Quite the contrary, she thought. But how would her husband take it?

The guilt she had borne all those years suddenly overwhelmed her and she pushed the snapshot across the table.

'Robert, I don't quite know how to . . . there's something I've got to tell you . . . something that happened before I met you . . .'

WRITING

Continue the story

Write a few lines saying what you think happened next.

_____
_____
_____
_____
_____

• Review •

GRAMMAR

Review of verb forms

Read the extract about Imran Khan, who used to be the cricket captain of Pakistan, and put the verbs in the correct form. Use a modal or a negative form where necessary. In some cases there is more than one possibility.

' I (1 *grow up*) _____grew up_____ in Lahore in a household full of women – my mother and three younger sisters. I was very much the man of the house so I (2 *say*) _____ it was a female-dominated atmosphere. In Pakistan the family unit is very strong and traditionally prospective brides (3 *study*) _____ carefully by the family. I remember that whenever a woman (4 *consider*) _____ for me, my sisters would have the last say. They never thought that anyone was good enough.

My mother impressed on me the value of honesty. I remember one incident when I was 13, when I ordered my chauffeur to let me (5 *drive*) _____. I (6 *spot*) _____ by a policeman who realised I was under-age. I bribed the policeman and got away. When I told my mother, she was furious that I (7 *face*) _____ the consequences.

When my mother (8 *die*) _____ of cancer four years ago, I realised that if someone with money (9 *suffer*) _____ so much then the poor have no chance. So in recent years I (10 *work*) _____ to set up the first cancer hospital in Pakistan (11 *give*) _____ free treatment to the poor.

My mother was disappointed she never saw me married. She (12 *have*) _____ a couple of candidates in mind, but either my sisters vetoed them or I (13 *object*) _____. At that time I (14 *always, travel*) _____ a lot and never seemed to have any time. There was only one occasion that I came near, when I (15 *involve*) _____ with an English girl, and I thought I (16 *marry*) _____ her. Sadly, it didn't happen. I realised how impossible it (17 *be*) _____ if we had got married to make it work, with half my time spent in England and half in Lahore. (18 *adapt*) _____ to life in Pakistan would have been like asking for the sky from her.

Even though I (19 *now, leave*) _____ international cricket I'm sure I (20 *go on*) _____ spending my summers in England. It's like the end of a love affair: it's not immediately possible to fall in love again. '

(from *Woman's Journal*)

Conditionals; *wish*

Complete the following sentences.

a) 'Your car's covered in snow this morning.'
  'Yes. I wish I ___*had put it away*___ last night.'

b) 'Pam says she doesn't want to make a speech.'
  'It's crazy. If only _____ so shy.'

c) 'Pedro lost his tennis match because he didn't practise.'
  'If he _____, _____ won.'

d) 'The baby's making a lot of noise!'
  'Yes. I wish _____ stop crying.'

e) 'I hear you had a terrible holiday.'
  'It was OK but I wish we _____ at a better hotel.'

f) 'Will you come and see me this evening?'
  'I _____ unless you _____ dinner for me.'

g) 'I've got these awful pains in my chest.'
  'If I _____ you, I _____ the doctor.'

Modals

Underline the most likely alternative.

a) Not many people watch Cambridge United play. They *can't / mustn't / needn't* have a very good team.

b) I had my bag stolen. I *should have kept / must have kept* it in my desk but I didn't.

c) 'Do you shave?' 'No, I've got a beard so I *mustn't / shouldn't / don't have to.*

d) You *could have / may have* sent it to me by post. Why didn't you? You *mustn't have / needn't have / mightn't have* come in person.

e) I hear Saskia was very ill last night. *Did she have to go / Must she have gone* to hospital?

f) Her father left her a fortune when he died. He *might / should / must* have been very rich.

g) Somebody stole my car last night. It *mightn't / shouldn't / can't / mustn't* have been Steve. He was with me the whole time.

h) When I was sixteen I *could / can / might* swim very well.

Spot the errors

There is a grammatical error in each of the following sentences. Underline the error and then correct it. There may be more than one possibility.

a) I <u>checked my teeth</u> at the dentist's.
  I had my teeth checked at the dentist's.

b) When he doesn't hurry, I won't wait for him.
  _____

c) The money has spent on education.
  _____

d) He's an old friend of her.
  _____

e) He ordered that I left.
  _____

f) Please remember locking the door before you go out.
  _____

g) This room needs to paint.
  _____

Which is correct?

Underline the correct alternatives.

a) That's *very good advice / a very good advice.*

b) I've never seen *something / anything* like it.

c) Neither *them / of them* knew the answer.

d) She passed her exam *which pleased me / , which pleased me.*

e) That's the man *who / which / whose* daughter is a pop singer.

f) There's a bus *left / leaving / is leaving* in an hour's time.

g) She *said him / told him / told to him* to hurry up.

h) She wondered where *was I going / I was going.*

VOCABULARY

Colloquial language

Complete the sentences with words from the box.

> off hand nose fancy actions bell
> dark gold away up

a) _____ speak louder than words.

b) If you cheat you'll never get _____ with it.

c) I wanted to go but I've gone _____ the idea.

d) Let's sit down and see if we can come _____ with a new idea.

e) The situation is getting out of _____ and quite dangerous.

f) _____ seeing you here!

g) The children were as good as _____ while you were out.

h) That name rings a _____. Have we met before?

i) Shut up! It gets up my _____ when people say that!

j) We were kept completely in the _____ about his plans.

Test your vocabulary

Write the answers to these questions on a separate sheet of paper.

a) Before the word *forbidden* do we say *deeply* or *strictly*?

b) Do we comment *on* something or *in* something?

c) What do we call breaking into a house and stealing something?

d) What does *shelve* mean in a newspaper headline: *postpone* or *forget*?

e) *Fair* means *free from injustice*. What else does it mean?

f) What are the words for these mathematical symbols: + and − ?

g) What is the verb of the noun *reason*?

h) How do we describe an embarrassing mistake: a *faux pas* or a *cul-de-sac*?

i) Do we say a team *wins* or *beats* another team?

WRITING

Linking expressions

Read the first part of a magazine article and underline the correct alternatives.

> ### DON'T STAND SO CLOSE TO ME!
> I had an air of confidence (1) *because / so* why was I posing such a threat to all the men in the room?
>   The party was a great success. I, (2) *however, / but* was not. (3) *It / There* was something wrong.
>   I couldn't be sure, (4) *however, / but* I had the uncomfortable feeling that I was committing a social sin.
>   As a foreigner, I was, (5) *personally / of course*, likely to make the occasional embarrassing mistake. These, (6) *on the whole / as a result*, would be generously forgiven. (7) *Yet / That's why* one partner after another (mostly men) would gradually back away from me (8) *as soon as / until* a wall stopped them from running away.
>   Why this reaction? It puzzled me many years ago. (9) *Since / For* then, I have found out the reason why.

(by Helga Rettke-Grover)

Spelling

Read the second part of the article. There are ten spelling mistakes. Write the correct version in the gaps below.

> My misstake was not lerning the rules governing socal space in Britan. They are diferent here. Wen talking to peeple at parties, at work, or at meatings, I stoode far to close to them.

a) _____ b) _____

c) _____ d) _____

e) _____ f) _____

g) _____ h) _____

i) _____ j) _____

Punctuation

Rewrite the final part of the article on a separate sheet of paper, adding punctuation.

> the arabs stand closest to each other less than an elbow away the swedes stand farthest apart about an arm and a half in eastern europe people like each other at a wrists distance the latin folk dont mind at all if you move a lot closer just outside the length of your or their elbow whichever is the shorter the british someone said to me last week are best described as fingertip people and so are their american brothers and sisters.

Tapescripts

Unit 2

RECORDING 1

An interview with Pat

Extract 1

INTERVIEWER: Pat, do you think the way you were brought up influenced the way you brought your children up?

PAT: Oh definitely, yes. One silly thing is that I always wanted a party when I was younger and my mother – I mean I can see now, she was very very busy, and we were never allowed a party – so now my children always have these huge parties. Another thing is that I think I probably took much more interest in my children's upbringing – you know – wanted to know what they were doing in school, encouraged them to join clubs and was quite happy to drive them anywhere, for example if they had a violin lesson or a piano lesson, or wanted to go swimming – quite happy to drive them there, whereas my parents didn't show any interest really in us doing anything. And although my father had a car we would never have thought of asking him to drive us anywhere, we walked or got the bus.

I: Any other things that were different?

P: Well, yes – I think – well, my husband was much more involved with the children, and our relationship, and particularly his is much different to my relationship with my father. I mean, really, I don't know what to say to my father, whereas John's got a very, very good relationship with the children and shows them a great deal of affection. I mean, my children are now in their twenties, but – you know, still cuddle him and kiss him and all this, and I think it's very important, affection in families, and a hug and a cuddle will help a lot. And altogether our relationship is different – it's more informal and we can talk about things with our children that I'd never dream of mentioning in front of my parents.

Extract 2

INTERVIEWER: What do you think your best qualities are as parents?

PAT: I think I care very much for my children and so even if perhaps they did something that I didn't approve of I would always help them, as opposed to my parents only really want to know us in good times – you know, if things are going well and not if things are going badly. And John, I think it's because he's much more even than I am, and more consistent and he will – you know, if there's a problem he can discuss it without getting all upset, which is much better with young people – you get much further.

I: If you had your time again is there any way in which you'd change the way you brought them up?

P: Oh yes, loads. I wouldn't worry – I felt I worried far too much about education, but that was a reflection on my upbringing, where my education was really sort of messed about, and so I wanted to make sure that theirs wasn't, and that they got a good education and I think I focused too much on it. Because we were both young, I think, when we had the children we were growing up very much with them and things that I thought were very important then, I can see from this point of view, they're not now. Now I know that having young parents has some advantages but I do think that I'd make a better parent now, simply because I've got a more mature view of life. But having said that we've got two nice children and I enjoy being with them.

Unit 3

RECORDING 1

Here is a summary of the news.

The Prime Minister has just announced that there will not be a January election. He was speaking at the opening of Parliament a few minutes ago. His speech is still going on.

Police have found the toddler who disappeared from her home a week ago. Detectives in Oxford have been questioning people all week in connection with the abduction but so far no one has been charged.

The economic situation is finally beginning to improve, according to figures which were released yesterday.

Unemployment has also been falling gradually over the last few months and export figures reached their highest level last month.

Unit 4

RECORDING 1

A radio programme about Las Vegas

ANNOUNCER: Last week Mike Davies visited Las Vegas, in Nevada, USA, and brings us this report from the land of the casinos.

MD: Las Vegas is a casino empire with yearly revenues of over six billion dollars. This is where America lets its hair down, and gambling has the status of an official religion. The industry greets you like a salesman the moment you step off the plane. Fruit machines in the Arrivals Hall, the sound of handles, reels spinning, and the sound of dollars cascading into trays. And in Departures video poker as far as you can see, as people wait reluctantly for their planes.

Downtown, in the suburban luxury, the dominance of the big casinos is absolute. If you don't like gambling stay out of Vegas, is the clear message. The city, with its swelling population of more than 700,000, is built on the proposition that every American likes to chance his luck.

The city centre is in fact a collection of casinos, motels, souvenir shops, porn cinemas and pawnbrokers. Occasionally a spire intrudes – the churches are unusually well-attended – but the wise clergyman knows which subjects are best avoided on Sundays. Much of the city looks like a parking lot – areas of concrete which mock the meaning of its Spanish name: The Meadows.

RECORDING 2

Mike Davies continues

Caesars Palace, the most famous casino theme-park, describes itself as an opulent Greco-Roman fantasy land and the 85 acre complex is, in appearance, a cross between a re-creation of the Roman forum, with Greek additions, and a multi-storey car park. It's approached by moving walkways of white marble, overlooking fountains and palm trees. Throughout, there are enormous reproductions of classical statues – especially of Julius Caesar.

The actual gambling goes on 24 hours a day, 365 days a year. Roulette, baccarat, craps, pontoon and poker are all played for stakes that can sometimes exceed $100,000, under the practised gaze of dealers, bankers and security men. There are also a variety of different machines. 'We pick our machines each morning and we stay on 'em,' one retired Alabaman told me. 'I figure, by the end of the day, it owes me.' His wife is doing better than him. She feeds in handfuls of dollar tokens and with surprising regularity the machine is sick over her, spewing out as much as $20 a time. A small tub is already three-quarters full of her winnings.

'I just love Caesars,' she confesses, needlessly. 'We come here three or four times a year.'

It turns out that they once won $600 but their goal remains the Big One.

Two years previously a housewife from Detroit won spectacularly. There had been no big winners for some time and the jackpot stood at $2 million when she pulled the lever. The money literally engulfed her, but she didn't go crazy. She bought a mink coat, had champagne for breakfast and had her hair done at the casino salon. Then she went home to Michigan.

These days there's even a zone for the elderly, on the banks of the Colorado River. Here, senior citizens, with their wealth of savings and a reckless urge to 'do it just one more time' park their caravans and move inside to 'work the machines'. So far there's no children's version planned – but if it does ever happen it'll be in Vegas and nowhere else. You can bet your bottom dollar.

ANNOUNCER: Next week we'll be hearing from Felicity Marsh, on safari in Zimbabwe, Until then, goodbye for now.

Unit 6

RECORDING 1

An interview between a doctor and a patient

Extract 1

DOCTOR: And what's the trouble?

PATIENT: I've got a bad back. I woke up one morning and I just found I really couldn't move without causing sort of like quite a lot of pain . . . and I work a lot on a word processor and continuously sitting in one position is proving to be very, very painful. I'm having to get up and move around.

D: Which part of your back is feeling . . . which part's feeling painful?

P: It's the lower part of my back.

D: Right. Have you had any trouble like that before?

P: I had a riding accident quite a few years ago and I, I fell off and actually landed in the sitting position and it was very painful for a few days but then it went away, but I find things can trigger it off again.

D: And how would you describe the pain?

P: It feels really tense . . . like a sort of like a tightening of all the muscles of the lower back and going down to the top of my legs.

D: It does go down your legs as well.

P: Yeah, it does. Just . . . to the top of them.

D: And have you noticed anything else makes its worse? You've talked about leaning over your word processor.

P: Yes, standing up in one position. If I go to a rugby match or something and I'm standing up for a period of time, then I find that that starts to cause pain in my lower back.

Extract 2

DOCTOR: Have you had treatment for it in the past?

PATIENT: No, I took some painkillers when I when, I first had, had the accident but it, it went away quite, quite soon when it was. I just thought it was normal because having sort of fallen off my horse I thought well this is going to hurt. I didn't think it was anything sort of out of the ordinary, just bruising.

D: But ever since that time you've had a tendency to get trouble back again.

P: Yes, it just it flares up every so often, it's not a constant thing and it never really lasts for more than a few days.

D: And with what's happening at the moment obviously we need to check you out but have you ever had any physiotherapy or anything like that to help you with back exercises?

P: No, I've, I've had . . . I've done some back exercises but I've never had any any physio.

D: Right . . .

Extract 3

DOCTOR: We'd better just check up by getting your back X-rayed just to see whether there's any damage that you actually sustained at the time of the injury.

PATIENT: Right.

D: And I think we could certainly give you a course of more effective pain relief . . .

P: Right.

D: . . . and also arrange for some physiotherapy and see whether we can really get on top of this problem for you and stop it incapacitating you as it obviously has started to do.

P: And in the meantime is it advisable to not sort of over-exert myself like with the aerobics and things?

D: I think if you know there are definite movements which aggravate it at the moment it would be wiser not to . . .

P: Right.

D: . . . because at the end of the day if you go and get a really bad incapacitating attack you're going to have to – you know, rest completely.

Unit 8

RECORDING 1

A dialogue between astronaut John Glenn and Mission Control

JOHN GLENN: Heading towards daybreak. A lot of cloud coverage today. Man, it's beautiful . . .

MISSION CONTROL 1: Possibly it's the heat shield. It's loose. If it comes off, it'll burn up.

MC2: They'll fry when he tries to re-enter.

MC3: John, can you hear me? Friendship 7, come in, please.

MC4: Let's try something. Anything.

JG: Friendship 7. This is Friendship 7. Do you read me? Over. I see something strange out here. Oh, my goodness gracious. What the heck is that? Sparks, needles of some kind, all over the sky. This is Friendship 7. Let me tell you what I'm in up here. I'm in a mass of some very small particles that are brilliantly lit up. I never saw anything like it. A whole shower of them coming by me now. They're bright, bright yellow. They're all lit up. They swarm around the capsule and they go in front of the window and they're brilliantly lit. You don't think these things could be alive do you? They look like fireflies on a summer night. They just dance around. Oh, oh. Maybe some airforce experiment that went wrong or something. Do you read me? This is miraculous.

MC: Roger, Friendship 7. Can you relate the actions of the particles surrounding your spacecraft with the action of your control jets? Do you read? Over.

JG: Negative. I do not think they were coming from my control jet. That's a negative. Over. . . . You guys all probably think I'm nuts down there. They're very beautiful. Get out of here. Get out of here. Heading into daybreak now. Another day. Leaving the fireflies behind. Have no idea what they were. This is Friendship 7.

MC1: He's going to restart orbit. How much longer are you going to keep him in the dark?

MC2: What we're going to tell him?

MC1: He's a pilot. You tell him the condition of his craft.

MC2: John, you're going to try right now for re-entry. We recommend you do the best you can to keep a zero angle. Over.

JC: Re-entry. Only three orbits? Over.

MC1: That is correct. Over.

JG: Do you have any reason for this? Over.

MC1: Not at this time. This is the judgement of Cape Flights.

JG: Roger.

RECORDING 2

A horoscope for Cancer

This is likely to be an important week, with the challenge of change in the air, mixed with unusual opportunities and a number of fortunate coincidences. You should be keen to go; if you do not make a move you could lose your chance.

RECORDING 4

The complete horoscope for Leo

You'll be in a difficult mood, determined to be different just for the sake of it. Friends will find you entertaining but annoying; your social life will be lively but you'll almost certainly be offered advice you have no patience with.

Unit 12

RECORDING 1

Part of a radio programme about homicide

Extract 1

Fortunately for the police, killers rarely plan the deed. Few murders are committed in cold, calculating blood. More than half the homicides every year take place because of quarrels, revenge or loss of temper and that's the official classification. The result is not carefully tailored violence but overkill and Dr West has seen it time and time again: 'Most homicides are unpremeditated, done on the spur of the moment, often associated with the use of alcohol or maybe drug related. Most of them occur in the domestic situation, or in the situation where individuals are known to each other. Where a sudden fit of passion is involved and the attack becomes frenzied there is usually repeated injury. In most deaths, homicidal deaths, far more violence than is actually required to effect death or serious harm is actually employed.

Extract 2

'We had on one occasion a typical instance of people being volatile when there was an argument over a parking space and three people were stabbed by one chap who was upset over having his parking place pinched by this other group, and he took a plain common or garden knife from a table in a restaurant and stabbed at three people, two through the heart, two of whom died . . .'

That incident, the quarrel over the parking place, appalling though it was, sticks in the memory precisely because it was so unusual. In many cities in the United States it would be nothing. In America there are over twenty thousand homicides every year. If we had that sort of mayhem on our streets there'd be thousands of victims, not just 685. We're still a law-abiding nation, like the rest of Europe, and guns are not readily available except, of course, in Northern Ireland. Murder in that small part of the United Kingdom is dominated by the gun.

Unit 14

RECORDING 1

Part of a radio programme about bad manners

ANNOUNCER: Examples of bad manners. When they're asked for, people do tend to come up with much the same examples, whoever they are. First of all what do the pundits nominate?

SPEAKER 1:   Inconsideration for others; not thanking you when you hold a door open for them – just being rude and uncooperative really annoys me; shop assistants who talk to each other when you're standing there with the money held out dying to pay. One almost feels like walking off and risk being had up for shoplifting sometimes. That really bugs me.

SPEAKER 2:   The things that really annoy me about modern manners are really the kind of selfishness which gets nobody anywhere. For example, people trying to push on to trains before other people have got off them, because that does no good to the person getting on and it's extremely annoying for those trying to get off.

SPEAKER 3:   The one that really irritates me more than anything I think is when I'm trying to find a parking spot and someone creeps in behind me and gets it and I've been queuing for it. That really does annoy me. It's so unfair. And usually it's a man that does it and I do object to that strongly.

SPEAKER 4:   I don't like to see people eating out of chip, chip papers in the town and I wouldn't do it.

SPEAKER 5:   I don't think it hurts anyone to say 'Yes, please', 'No, thank you'. I mean I was brought up to say that but I don't think children are taught that now cos mums seem to be so busy the children are stuck in front of the telly with the tea on their knee while mum is doing something else.

SPEAKER 6:   It varies though with the manners, doesn't it? I mean the old are as bad as the young. If you're at a bus queue – I mean I'm a pensioner myself – and they will push to get in, push the youngsters out and after all's said and done they're as much right to get on the bus or on the train as what we are.

ANNOUNCER: Motoring manners are rather special because people who might be politeness itself when they're being pedestrians can be turned into monsters of depravity once they're safely – as they might think – inside a suit of armour or in this case a four-wheeled tin box.

SPEAKER 7:   I do think a lot of people when they get behind the wheel change character almost – I think I do to some extent quite honestly – and would shake a fist at somebody or even shout at somebody who I wouldn't – I wouldn't dream of doing that if they were standing next to me. But from the confines of the car it seems quite safe really.

Unit 16

RECORDING 1

Helen, Dick and Chris are talking about sport

HELEN: Even for somebody who doesn't really understand the rules particularly well, it's quite easy to work out what's going on, to follow the action from one end of the pitch to the other. I suppose really the most exciting moments in any match are when your team get a free kick or a penalty kick even and get the chance to score a goal. I, . . . when they score a goal, which is the only way they can win, that has to be the best moment. I mean for some people it's the highlight of the entire week when your, when your team score a goal and, even though it's great to see a really skilful or spectacular goal, in the end it doesn't matter how they get that ball over the goal line as long as it goes into the back of the net.

DICK: What I like about going to the games now is the atmosphere because it reminds me of all the things I remember from when I started going to games as a kid. First of all there's the anticipation

as you push into the stadium with the rest of the crowd and then once inside there's the hot sun and the smell of beer and the smell of the hot dogs – everybody eats hot dogs at the game – and there's the calls of the vendors moving through the stands selling food and drink. Now, of course, the object of the game is to hit the ball and if, if nobody hits the ball the game can seem, can seem very slow and drag on a long time . . . One of the most exciting plays I think for me is, is when a ball is hit a long way, high in the air and a fielder has to run back catching it against the wall over his shoulder.

CHRIS: It's quite an emotional thing to see two, three hundred, two or three thousand people even, running. It's interesting to see the leaders, the athletes, of course, but I prefer to watch the strugglers, the ones who are coming up, maybe they've got another half an hour to run but there're going to do it and cheering them on and being cheered on is a great thing. Also, watching so many people running and everyone is wearing different running shoes or different shorts, etc. It's, it's a very colourful event, especially in the winter. They're running through drab countryside and you have this blaze of reds, greens, oranges. Wonderful colours, everybody's wearing a different colour. Also the courses, every course, every route is different; some are very flat, some you have to go round twice, so you get an opportunity to see all the runners twice.

Unit 17

RECORDING 1

A radio programme about foxhunting

SIMON BATES: The unspeakable in pursuit of the uneatable. That's how Oscar Wilde described foxhunting. The Hunt Saboteurs' Association has twelve active groups throughout the season. Why? Earlier today I phoned the Association's secretary, Bob August.

BOB AUGUST: The particular practices in question are so obnoxious that there must come a time when they will be outlawed, but until such time it was felt that something had to be done to give some relief to the quarry that were being chased and killed.

SB: On the other hand, those people who support hunting would say that there's a need to control wild animals that damage crops and livestock.

BA: That's a very debatable argument because statistically about sixty or seventy per cent of the country is under arable produce – you're producing grain crops and whatever – and under those circumstances foxes particularly are actually a boon to the farmer. The only problem of foxes, maybe – and yet again that's debatable – is chickens and sheep. Well, quite frankly, the vast majority of chickens are shut up in dirty great big battery houses now.

RECORDING 2

The programme continues

SIMON BATES: Would anybody suffer if groups like the Animal Liberation Front got their way? Is there evidence that farmers benefit from field sports?

FARMER: Well, yes, without a doubt they do. For one thing, we do suffer from predators, in particular the fox, and if you have sheep or lambs it can be a great menace. Hunting is the most humane way of exercising control – it's much more efficient than gassing or shooting them. However, nobody wants to eliminate foxes completely, of course, otherwise we'd be over-run by rabbits and suchlike. It's part of the natural balance of nature.

SB: Is it possible for contemporary agriculture to exist without field sports of some kind?

F: It could exist but I think the countryside would suffer as a result. Developers are constantly destroying the fox's habitat to build new roads and buildings. We hunters stop that happening, and we also plant small woodlands for foxes to live in. We have invested millions of pounds in this way.

RECORDING 3

The programme continues

SIMON BATES: I want to get Felicia from Cheshire in. Hallo.

FELICITY: Hallo.

SB: Have you ever hunted?

F: Yes.

SB: When?

F: When I was nine.
SB: And did you enjoy it?
F: The first time it was sort of a family event and so I went out, and the first time it really petrified me because when the lead hound caught the fox it just ripped it to pieces.
SB: Were you there?
F: Yes, and then afterwards my uncle wiped blood on my forehead.
SB: Now why did he do that?
F: Well, it's a tradition, and every new member has to have it done.
SB: I see. And did you like that?
F: No.
SB: Would you consider yourself a pro or an anti now?
F: Anti.
SB: OK. Thank you very much indeed.

Unit 19

RECORDING 1

The story continues

As he walked back to the Town Hall doubts and fears scurried around his head like cornered rats. It was just too damned close to be coincidence any more. For *he* used to run an MG, and *he* had married twenty years ago.

He could not concentrate at the office. An hour before finishing time, he got his car from the staff car park and drove to his semi in a leafy suburb on the outskirts of town.

Margaret, his wife, was doing some work in the garden. 'Robert, is that you? You're early. Nothing wrong at the office, is there?'

No, of course not.' Why did women always think the worst? 'I thought I'd finish off that lampstand in the shed while there's still some daylight.'

Right-o! I'll call you when dinner's ready.'

He put the inside catch on the shed door and made sure his wife was still in the front garden. Then he got a metal box from behind his workbench.

The key to the box was hidden under a bottle of weedkiller. Inside the box were two yellowing clippings from the *Elmston Observer*.

One was headlined: *Girl, 10, killed in hit-and-run.*

For the umpteenth time he read how the girl had been knocked down on a pedestrian crossing while on her way home from a schoolfriend's house.

The details were embedded in his memory. He had driven over to Margaret's parents' house in the MG that evening. They had lived just outside Elmston then.

Because of some road works, the traffic had been diverted.

He had been exceeding the speed limit, too. It was an unfamiliar route and the crossing had taken him by surprise.

The car's brakes were slack because he had skipped a service to save money, and a shower had made the road surface slippery . . .

Even though it was twenty years ago, he could still remember the sickening thud . . . the scream . . . the crumpled body on the side of the road.

Of course, he should have stopped, but he had panicked. He had been short-listed for a new job for which a clean driving licence was a condition of employment and it was only days away from his wedding. Reporting the incident would have ruined everything.

The second clipping, headed *Police appeal for witnesses*, said several people had heard the screech of brakes but none had seen the accident.

A police spokesman was quoted as saying they were 'pursuing several lines of enquiry'.

He locked the clippings away again and returned the box to its hiding place. He had never fully understood why he had kept them all these years. What, he wondered, would the psychologists make of that? A guilt complex, perhaps? A subconscious desire to punish himself for his crime?

It was his favourite tuna-fish salad for dinner but the memory of the accident had dulled his appetite. He pecked away at it, nodding absently as Margaret related the events of her day.

All through the meal the thought kept hammering in his brain: how long before the girl found out that *he* was the hit-and-run driver?

More than likely she was a former schoolfriend wanting to see justice done. Or a relative . . . the dead girl's sister, even.

The police enquiries had no doubt fizzled out years ago – they would have far more pressing cases on their plate – but the little girl's family and friends would not have given up the search.

RECORDING 2

The story continues

It was not until he and Margaret were watching TV that evening that the answer came to him; in fact, it was staring him in the face . . .

On the piano was an ornately framed picture of him and Margaret on their wedding day. Of course! Why hadn't he thought of it sooner? The other photos in the album; there was one of the MG.

He found the album and flicked through it. There it was – the pair of them, snapped in an MG as they were leaving the reception to go off on honeymoon.

He stared at himself from twenty years ago: thin face, unlined, thick curling hair. Now he had a double chin, was balding, wore a moustache and bifocals. Unrecognisable.

On the back of the MG was a 'Just married' placard, which obscured the middle two digits of the rear numberplate.

The girl must have gone to every photographer in the district until she found the one who had taken their wedding pictures. The negatives would have been on file, probably in a storeroom.

The girl had got a print. Then she had searched the *Evening Gazette's* back issues for the paper's own picture of the same couple in the MG . . . which would tell her the names and parents' addresses.

And there the search would stop, for Margaret's parents had emigrated long ago and his own parents were dead. He was safe.

Then it struck him like a blow. 'The electoral roll,' he said out loud. 'She simply goes through it, street by street, until she finds my name . . .'

'Did you say something, Robert?' Margaret called.

'What? No, nothing.'

It would only be a matter of time now before his skeleton was out of the cupboard. He would be branded a child-killer, all the more heinous because he had covered his tracks (he had sold the MG immediately they had got back from honeymoon).

He would get at least five years for manslaughter. He would lose his job; his reputation would be ruined; everything he had built up over the years . . . down the drain!

He knew he had not got the strength of character to begin all over again; he was too set in his ways.

'I think I'll go to *The Swan* for a pint, love. Don't wait up. I might be late.'

'Oh, all right. I'll leave something out for your supper.'

At times like this, he mused, it was positively an advantage having a conventionally predictable spouse.

It was a fifteen-minute drive to the block of service flats where the girl was staying; hers was on the ground floor.

She came to the door in a dressing-gown with a towel wrapped round her hair.

He was sorry to barge in on her unannounced, he blurted; but he had found himself in the neighbourhood, so he had thought he would give her that information about his friend.

'Oh, well, come in. You'll have to forgive my appearance – I'm in the middle of washing my hair. Can I get you a drink?'

'I won't thanks – I'm driving.'

'Ah yes . . . the old breathalyser.'

He tried to smile but couldn't move his face muscles. 'That friend,' he began, swallowing. 'His name's . . . Smythe . . . Robert Smythe.'

'That's it,' she cried. 'The same one I've been looking for! I found his address this afternoon, in the electoral roll at the Town Hall.'

So it was true, he thought; she was tracking him down.

'Perhaps I will have that drink,' he said, slipping a hand into his jacket pocket.

She was at the drinks cabinet, her back to him. 'Gin and tonic all right?'

'Fine.' He pulled out a length of cord. It went round her neck so easily. He did not make a sound as he pulled it tight. Nor did she . . .

Answer key

Unit 10, page 36

The invented story is number 3.

Unit 18, page 65

a)   Ben Johnson
b)   salt
c)   Dustin Hoffman
d)   Bermuda Triangle
e)   there isn't enough sun